The Open University

T357
Structural integrity:
designing against failure

BLOCK 2
FRACTURE MECHANICS
PART 6

This publication forms part of an Open University course T357 *Structural integrity: designing against failure*. Details of this and other Open University courses can be obtained from the Student Registration and Enquiry Service, The Open University, PO Box 197, Milton Keynes MK7 6BJ, United Kingdom: tel. +44 (0)845 300 60 90, email general-enquiries@open.ac.uk

Alternatively, you may visit the Open University website at http://www.open.ac.uk where you can learn more about the wide range of courses and packs offered at all levels by The Open University.

To purchase a selection of Open University course materials visit http://www.ouw.co.uk, or contact Open University Worldwide, Michael Young Building, Walton Hall, Milton Keynes MK7 6AA, United Kingdom for a brochure. tel. +44 (0)1908 858793; fax +44 (0)1908 858787; email ouw-customer-services@open.ac.uk

The Open University
Walton Hall, Milton Keynes
MK7 6AA

First published 2007.

Edited and designed by The Open University.

Typeset by SR Nova Pvt. Ltd, Bangalore, India.

Printed in the United Kingdom by The University Press, Cambridge.

ISBN 978 0 7492 2423 3

1.1

PART 6
CASE STUDIES

CONTENTS

1	**INTRODUCTION**	**7**
2	**REFINING THE DESIGN OF A LIFTING HOOK**	**8**
	2.1 Examining the stress distribution	9
	2.1.1 Using straight-beam theory	10
	2.1.2 Using curved-beam theory	11
	2.2 Improving the design geometry	14
	2.3 Comparing the design with the standard specification	15
	2.4 Proof stressing	17
3	**DESIGNING AGAINST CREEP RUPTURE**	**18**
	3.1 Creep revisited	18
	3.2 Creep rupture testing	19
	3.3 Summary	22
4	**FAILURE OF COMPOSITE PRODUCTS**	**23**
	4.1 Structure of composite materials	25
	4.1.1 Glass-reinforced plastic	28
	4.1.2 Applications of glass-reinforced plastic	29
	4.2 Storage tanks	30
	4.2.1 Choice of materials	30
	4.2.2 Mechanisms of failure	35
	4.3 Tank failure case study	37
	4.3.1 Reinvestigation of the failure	38
	4.3.2 Tank specification	39
	4.3.3 Dimensions of the wall	42
	4.3.4 Reassembly of the parts	44
	4.3.5 Fracture surface	45
	4.3.6 Tank fill history	46
	4.3.7 Materials behaviour	48
	4.3.8 Conclusions	51
5	**CODA**	**53**
	LEARNING OUTCOMES	**53**
	ANSWERS TO EXERCISES	**54**
	ANSWERS TO SELF-ASSESSMENT QUESTIONS	**56**
	ACKNOWLEDGEMENTS	**63**

1 INTRODUCTION

This final part of T357 uses case studies to revisit some of the concepts that I have introduced in the course and exposes you to some additional factors that may be involved when particular material types are employed.

An important message that you should take with you from T357 is that there is a need to understand how materials will behave when they are exposed to the precise combination of loads, residual stresses, temperatures and chemical environments that occur in service – and that considering only a subset of these is asking for trouble. The case studies in this part should help to demonstrate this.

The first case study returns to the lifting hook that I originally introduced in Block 1 Part 1, looking at how the basic design can be modified so that it is closer to the specification for a load-bearing hook given in the British Standards. After that, I revisit the topic of creep that I introduced in Block 1 Part 7, looking in particular at creep rupture in polymer pipes for gas distribution. In the third case study I move on to examine the kinds of failure that can occur in composite materials, using the specific example of a storage tank to illustrate some of the factors that need to be considered when using such materials in service.

2 REFINING THE DESIGN OF A LIFTING HOOK

Back in Block 1 Parts 1 and 2 we looked at the stress distribution in a simple load-bearing hook. The idea was to illustrate the way in which a uniaxial load can lead to a complex (i.e. non-uniaxial) state of stress in a component of non-uniform geometry. You weren't asked to carry out any detailed analysis of the hook itself, which was of a very simple design, but I did show you the results from a finite-element simulation (Figure 6.1a) and from a photoelastic model (Figure 6.1b), in order to illustrate the nature of the overall two-dimensional stress distribution. Significant tensile and compressive stresses occur within the curved part of the hook, much larger than those in the straight neck, and you should now appreciate that these arise largely as a result of bending.

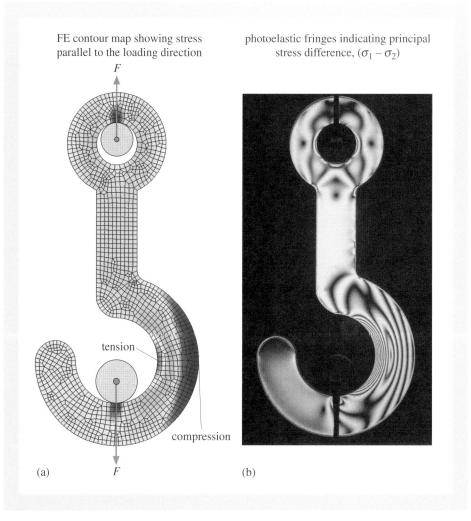

FE contour map showing stress parallel to the loading direction

photoelastic fringes indicating principal stress difference, $(\sigma_1 - \sigma_2)$

F

tension

compression

(a) F (b)

Figure 6.1 Stress distribution in a two-dimensional hook geometry: (a) finite-element simulation; (b) photoelastic model

However, you may have recognized that the geometry shown in Figure 6.1 looks more like that of a catch from a cupboard door than that of a load-bearing hook! In this section I want you to take a closer look at how the design can be modified so that it is better able to carry a significant load, drawing on your knowledge of stress analysis and bending theory.

2.1 Examining the stress distribution

Let's consider modifying the initial design so that it can safely carry a load of 10 kN: that's equivalent to a mass of just over one tonne (1000 kg). The design specifications for forged load-bearing hooks are actually covered by British Standard BS 2903 *Specification for higher tensile steel hooks for chains, slings, blocks and general engineering purposes*. Following this standard, hooks are assigned a safe working load for which the maximum tensile stress in the hook is limited to 309 MPa. We'll work to the same guideline and aim to keep our maximum stress under this limit.

Although we have spent most of the course applying two-dimensional approximations of plane stress or plane strain, in this case we will need to think in three dimensions. I'll start by scaling up the initial hook geometry, making the width of the neck 30 mm, the inner and outer radii of the curved semicircular region 30 mm and 60 mm respectively, and assigning a uniform thickness of 12 mm, as illustrated in Figure 6.2. The geometry isn't exactly the same as before – the transition from the straight neck to the curved section is smoother, for example – but the way in which the bending stresses are generated across the middle of the curved hook is essentially the same.

We'll go back to what you already know about beams and bending in order to get an initial estimate of the maximum stresses that might arise during loading.

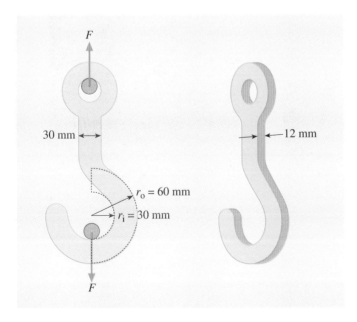

Figure 6.2
Three-dimensional hook geometry comprising a curved beam with rectangular cross section

Figure 6.3 Semicircular beam, part of the hook geometry of Figure 6.2, showing forces and bending moment acting on section AB

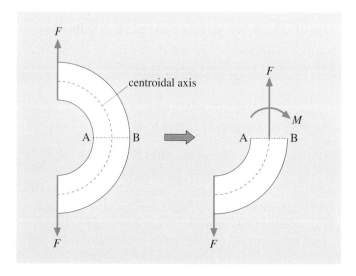

2.1.1 Using straight-beam theory

Consider the main curved part of the hook to take the form of a semicircular beam, shown as a dotted outline in Figure 6.2. I have redrawn this beam in Figure 6.3 to show that the applied loading not only gives rise to a force in the loading direction, but also applies a moment to the curved beam. We are most interested in the maximum stresses that occur across the midsection of the beam, along the dashed line AB in Figure 6.3. These stresses can be approximated by making the rather unrealistic assumption that the beam is *straight* and applying the engineer's bending equation, which you first met in Block 1 Part 6:

$$\frac{M}{I} = \frac{\sigma}{y} = \frac{E}{R} \tag{6.1}$$

Recall that, in this equation, the y-direction is taken to be perpendicular to the length of a straight beam. Hence, in Figure 6.3 the y-direction is *parallel* to section AB; σ is the normal stress *perpendicular* to AB.

SAQ 6.1 (Block 1 revision and learning outcome 6.1)

(a) Use the engineer's bending equation, Equation (6.1), to estimate the maximum and minimum bending stresses across section AB in Figure 6.3 for an applied load of 10 kN. Do this by applying the equation at the inner and outer radii, referring to the dimensions given in Figure 6.2 as necessary.

Recall from Block 1 Part 6 that for a straight beam under bending, the centroid of the beam (the centre of its cross-sectional area) coincides with the neutral surface (at which the bending stress is zero).

Remember:

the bending moment M is equal to the applied force F times the distance from the centre of curvature to the centroid of the beam

y is measured *with reference to the neutral surface* and is positive at the inner radius

the second moment of area I is equal to $bh^3/12$ for a solid rectangular section.

(b) The total stress at any point in the beam along section AB is actually the bending stress *plus* an additional stress due to direct tensile loading. The latter is due to the application of F acting over the whole cross-sectional area at AB. Calculate the maximum and minimum *total* stresses.

2.1.2 Using curved-beam theory

Making the approximation that our curved beam is straight indicates that the maximum tensile stress, which at any point is the sum of the normal bending stress and the direct applied tensile stress, is around 280 MPa. That's below our self-imposed design limit of 309 MPa, but the margin of difference is a little too narrow for comfort, given the crudeness of our approach.

In fact, you won't be surprised to hear that, although straight-beam theory works reasonably well for a beam with a shallow curve, a large degree of curvature can lead to significant errors. That's because, in the case of a curved beam subjected to pure bending, the tensile–compressive stress distribution across the thickness of the beam is no longer linear, and the position of the neutral surface no longer coincides with the centroid of the beam. More specifically, the neutral surface is displaced towards the centre of curvature. This is illustrated in Figure 6.4 for a curved beam of rectangular cross section, where the offset e is defined as the difference between the centroidal radius, R, and the radius to the neutral surface, r_n.

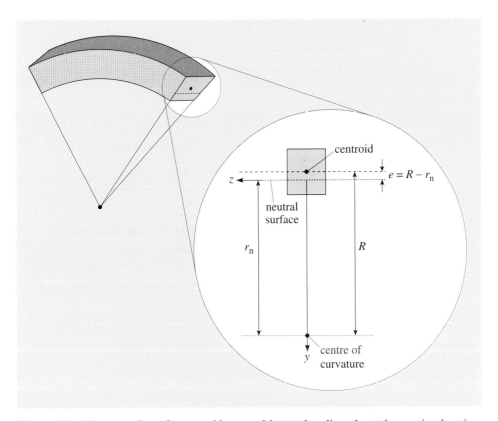

Figure 6.4 Cross section of a curved beam subject to bending about the z-axis, showing the offset of the neutral surface from the centroid

For a uniformly curved beam subjected to pure bending, the internal bending stresses can be determined from:

$$\sigma = \frac{My}{Ae(r_n - y)} \tag{6.2}$$

where A is the cross-sectional area and the offset e is equal to $R - r_n$. The difficulty of applying the curved-beam formula, Equation (6.2), lies in the evaluation of r_n; fortunately values for common cross sections are widely available. Some examples of these are given in Figure 6.5.

Let's see what difference using the curved-beam equation actually makes.

SAQ 6.2 (Learning outcome 6.2)

Using the formula for bending of a curved beam, Equation (6.2), determine the maximum and minimum normal stresses in the semicircular beam of the hook in Figure 6.2. Assume a 10 kN load.

Remember:

the bending moment M is equal to FR

y is measured from the neutral surface, so that at the inner radius $y = r_n - r_i$ and at the outer radius $y = r_n - r_o$ (see Figure 6.4)

don't forget to add the applied tensile stress to the bending stresses you compute.

Figure 6.5 Radius to neutral surface, r_n, for common cross-sectional shapes

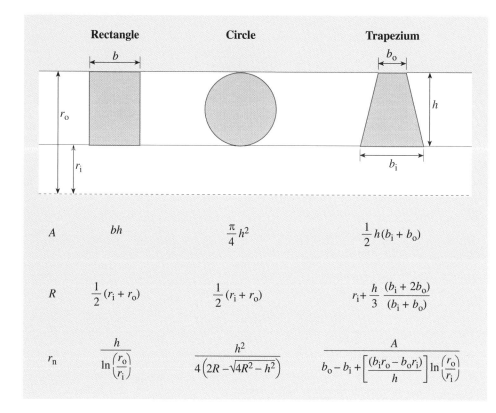

The answer to SAQ 6.2 shows that the total tensile stress at the inner radius is predicted to be 350 MPa, which is much larger than when we made the straight-beam assumption. Although the compressive stress at the outer radius is now 175 MPa, smaller than previously calculated, the maximum stress clearly exceeds our design limit of 309 MPa.

In Figure 6.6 I have plotted the stress distribution across the entire thickness of the hook for both the curved-beam and the straight-beam analyses. Note that the inner and outer radii of the beam are respectively at the far left and the far right of this plot. Although the two solutions overlap to some extent, particularly across the central half of the thickness, the nonlinearity of the curved-beam solution predicts that stresses are more tensile (more positive) at the inner and outer extremities of the cross section than they are under the straight-beam analysis. In other words, the straight-beam solution does not provide a conservative estimate of the maximum stress likely in a curved beam. This reinforces my earlier caution that misuse of the straight-beam equation can lead to serious errors: as a rule of thumb, it should not be applied where the radius of curvature is large compared with the breadth b of the cross section.

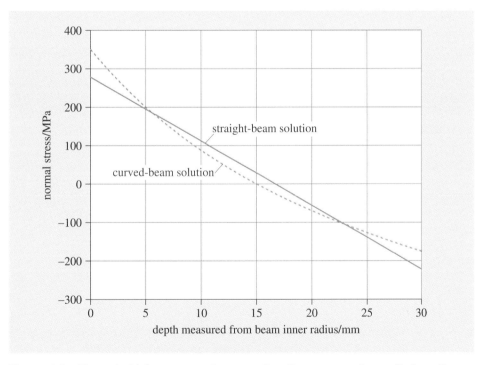

Figure 6.6   Through-thickness normal stresses (bending stresses plus applied tensile stresses) predicted for the hook using straight- and curved-beam theories

2.2 Improving the design geometry

We have found that the current geometry of the hook is not quite right for doing the job to our chosen specification – but we're not far off. Let's look at how we can tweak the design to get some improvement without increasing the amount of metal needed to make the hook.

SAQ 6.3 (Learning outcome 6.3)

How would you alter the cross-sectional shape of the beam, without changing the cross-sectional area, in order to produce a more favourable through-thickness stress distribution?

Bearing the answer to SAQ 6.3 in mind, it would make sense to redistribute the material so that it has a cross section in the shape of a trapezium (see Figure 6.5). This puts more material, and so lower stress, in the tensile bending region. If we make the thickness at the inner radius, b_i, equal to 18 mm and that at the outer radius, b_o, equal to 6 mm, then the cross-sectional area will be identical to that of our 12 mm by 30 mm rectangle and we will therefore use exactly the same mass of metal in the beam. In profile, the hook looks the same as before, as shown in Figure 6.7.

Let's see if the change in cross-sectional shape reduces the stresses as we would hope.

SAQ 6.4 (Learning outcome 6.2)

Estimate the *maximum* stress in the curved part of the hook if it has a trapezoidal cross section with dimensions as shown in Figure 6.7, assuming a 10 kN load.

The maximum stress in the beam is now estimated to be just under our design limit. The change in geometry has reduced it by about 13%, from 350 MPa down to just

Figure 6.7   Three-dimensional hook geometry comprising a curved beam with trapezoidal cross section

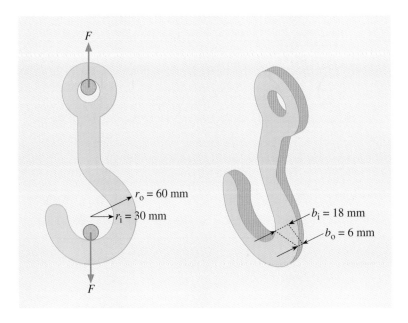

over 300 MPa. So with a simple modification we have come up with a design for a one-tonne-capacity hook that nominally meets the British Standard specification with regard to the maximum stress it experiences under loading.

2.3 Comparing the design with the standard specification

In fact, the standard for engineering steel hooks lays down very specific guidelines about every aspect of the hook geometry. Figure 6.8 is taken directly from BS 2903 and shows the geometry for a 'point hook with eye', intended for use with a chain hoist. Don't worry about the actual magnitude of the labelled dimensions in the figure; the point is that the drawing is to scale, so any hook made to this BS specification should look exactly like this. You will notice straight away that the load-bearing curved beam has a tapered cross section, a bit like a trapezium but with rounded corners – obviously, removing sharp edges reduces dangerous stress concentrations. But the standard geometry differs from our design in other ways.

EXERCISE 6.1

Compare the British Standard hook geometry in Figure 6.8 with our tapered hook geometry in Figure 6.7. Aside from subtle variations in cross-sectional shape, there are two significant overall differences between the two designs. Identify these two differences and their likely implications.

In the text of BS 2903, *all* the critical dimensions are specified as a function of the internal diameter, labelled C in Figure 6.8. For example, the width of the beam, H,

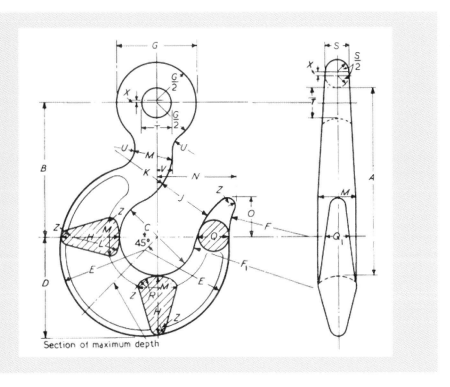

Section of maximum depth

Figure 6.8   Geometry of a point hook with eye, taken from BS 2903

is equal to 0.78C. The width of the beam in our hook design is $r_o - r_i = 30$ mm. So, to bring our hook geometry into closer agreement with the British Standard specification we should use an internal diameter of 30 mm/0.78, which is approximately 38 mm. That means an internal radius r_i of 19 mm. Keeping the overall thickness and cross section the same, and truncating the neck region, means we end up with a design for our lifting hook as shown in Figure 6.9.

So how does this new design perform? If you like you can calculate the maximum and minimum values yourself, but Figure 6.10 indicates that reducing the internal radius reduces the limiting stresses considerably, compared with our previous designs. The figure shows that altering the shape of the cross-sectional area from rectangular to trapezoidal had the effect of uniformly making the stresses more negative (more compressive) right through the beam section. This means that although the tensile stresses are reduced, the *magnitude* of the compressive stresses is increased. On the other hand, reducing the internal beam radius (and thus reducing the bending moment) lowers the magnitude of both tensile and compressive stresses. The maximum stress for the new design is 253 MPa, which is well within our initial design limit of 309 MPa; the corresponding minimum stress is −138 MPa.

Figure 6.9   Modified hook design with reduced inner radius and short neck

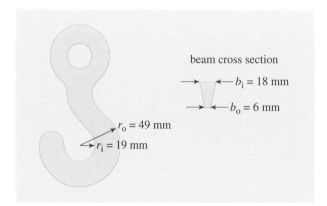

Figure 6.10   Through-thickness normal stresses for our various hook designs, assessed using curved-beam theory

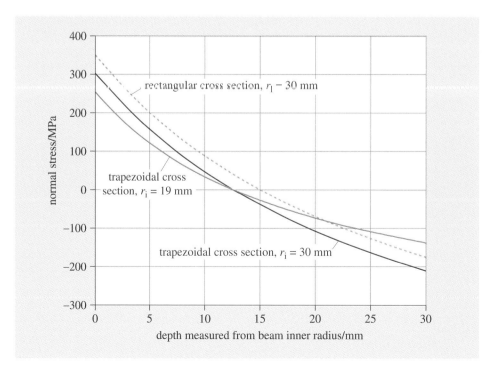

2.4 Proof stressing

Thus far, really rather subtle changes in design have led to a more compact geometry, better able to sustain the applied loading. However, one further improvement to the load-bearing capacity of the hook can be implemented that has nothing to do with altering the geometry. As part of the BS 2903 specifications, before it is used in service a working lifting hook is required to be proof loaded to *twice* its nominal safe working load. That's 20 kN in this case, which will double the stresses in the beam – these will reach over 500 MPa in our final modified design. Typical recommended steels for use in such hooks are carbon steels with a yield stress of around 400 MPa. This means that proof stressing causes yield at the inner radius of the hook beam.

SAQ 6.5 (Block 1 revision)

Thinking back to what you have learned about residual stresses (Block 1 Part 7), how might proof stressing beyond the yield point at the hook inner radius lead to a beneficial final stress state in the hook cross section?

In fact, the final stress state in a lifting hook may not look quite like the stress profile we have calculated during this case study, as in reality it is a simple summation of the applied loading stress plus the residual stress variation from the proof stressing. Proof stressing ensures such a safe distribution of stresses in the beam part of the hook that, provided the BS specifications are adhered to, it is very unlikely that failure will occur there under normal use. However, the stress analysis and design procedure we have followed is still essential: without it, the proof-stressing procedure could not have been reliably established.

3 DESIGNING AGAINST CREEP RUPTURE

3.1 Creep revisited

I want to continue this series of case studies with a look at the sort of information that is important in designing against failure caused by creep damage.

Let's review briefly what we know about creep:

- It is a phenomenon by which a material undergoes a gradually increasing strain until failure.

- It occurs at stresses below the nominal yield stress of the material.

- It typically occurs at temperatures above $0.4T_m$, where T_m is the material's melting temperature in kelvin.

For most structural metals at room temperature, creep can effectively be neglected. However, this is not the case for all materials, as illustrated by Exercise 6.2.

You should recall that $T_H = T/T_m$; creep will typically occur for values of T_H greater than 0.4.

EXERCISE 6.2

Calculate the homologous temperature T_H for each of the following materials (where relevant, assume that room temperature is 25 °C). Is creep likely to occur in these cases?

(a) Steel (melting point 1400 °C) operating at 650 °C.

(b) A solder (melting point 190 °C) at room temperature.

(c) An aluminium alloy (melting point 540 °C) at room temperature.

(d) Polyethylene (melting point 130 °C) at room temperature.

The answer to Exercise 6.2 shows that creep can be as much a problem for some room-temperature applications as it is for the materials used for turbines in power generation or aeroengines. However, the seriousness of the problem inevitably increases with temperature. For this reason, clever materials alloying is used to improve the creep lives of alloys for very high-temperature applications, which may operate at homologous temperatures of 0.8 or higher.

In this section I will look briefly at a more mundane application: the pipework that is used to distribute gas around the UK. Such pipes are commonly made from polyethylene. They operate under a given internal pressure, and also have to bear loads associated with their own weight (if laid above ground and carried on supports) or from soil loading (if buried). As Exercise 6.2 showed, creep of the material is possible, and this is one of the factors that needs to be considered. The UK gas industry works to a 50-year life for pipes, so the challenge for the material is significant.

3.2 Creep rupture testing

To design an appropriate pipe for the purpose, we first need to know the time it takes for rupture to occur in different types of polyethylene, which of course will depend on the level of tensile stress acting on the material. This information is obtained by carrying out pressurization tests on short lengths of pipe; the samples are filled with water under a pressure that is kept constant (to ±2% accuracy) and the time taken to develop a leak is measured. The temperature of the pipe specimens is kept constant by immersing them in a temperature-controlled water bath.

EXERCISE 6.3

The method described above sounds like a complicated method for creep testing. Suggest why it is used in preference to performing a uniaxial tensile creep test.

Figure 6.11 shows a typical ductile creep rupture produced by pressure testing a pipe made from medium-density polyethylene (MDPE); the pipe has ballooned locally, necked down and split. The radius of curvature of the swelling is much smaller in the radial direction than it is in the longitudinal direction.

SAQ 6.6 (Learning outcome 6.4 and Block 1 revision)

In which direction would you have expected the line of fracture to lie in the pipe shown in Figure 6.11?

Given the answer to SAQ 6.6, why does creep rupture occur parallel to the hoop direction? From the shape of the 'balloon' in Figure 6.11, it is clear that the material stretched more in the hoop direction than the longitudinal direction. This process aligns the polymer molecules to a greater extent in the hoop direction. The material is then stronger in this direction and weaker in the longitudinal direction. The longitudinal stress can then cause tensile failure as the material's strength is exceeded.

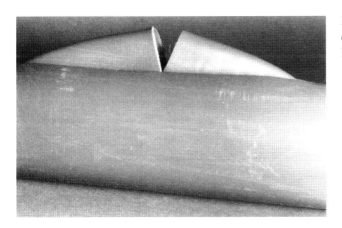

Figure 6.11 Typical ductile creep rupture in MDPE pipe

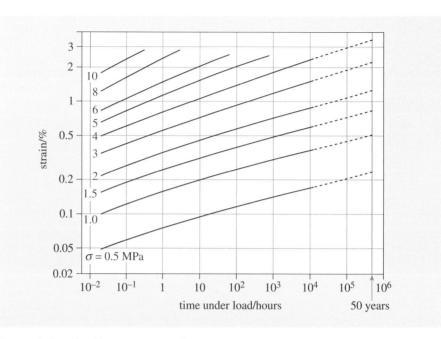

Figure 6.12   Tensile creep curves for an HDPE at 20 °C

Creep data tend not to be available for 50-year periods, so some extrapolation is needed. Figure 6.12 shows typical creep curves for a high-density polyethylene (HDPE), where the creep strains measured up to 10^4 hours (about two years) are extrapolated into the future.

Such creep data need to be used with care for polymers: the creep rate of a polymeric material can change if the polymer is stored at room temperature for several months before use, as its crystallinity and mechanical properties can change.

There can also be changes in the creep mechanism as creep progresses. Figure 6.13 shows the time to failure for an HDPE at a range of temperatures. You can see that in each case there is a change in the creep rate, occurring sooner at higher temperatures; this would not necessarily have been detected by a room-temperature creep test lasting, say, a year. Furthermore, after the transition, the failure mode becomes brittle rather than ductile.

> ## SAQ 6.7 (Learning outcome 6.5)
>
> (a) By extrapolation of the data in Figure 6.13, find the creep lifetime of the HDPE at 20 °C under a stress of (i) 5 MPa and (ii) 3 MPa.
>
> (b) Recommend an upper limit to the stress on the pipe that will allow it a 50-year life if it is to operate at 20 °C.

Typical in-service pipe pressures are between 7.5 kPa and 700 kPa, which would typically give hoop stresses in the wall of below 5 MPa, so the range of stresses shown in Figure 6.13 is an accurate indication of the conditions that may be found in working gas pipes.

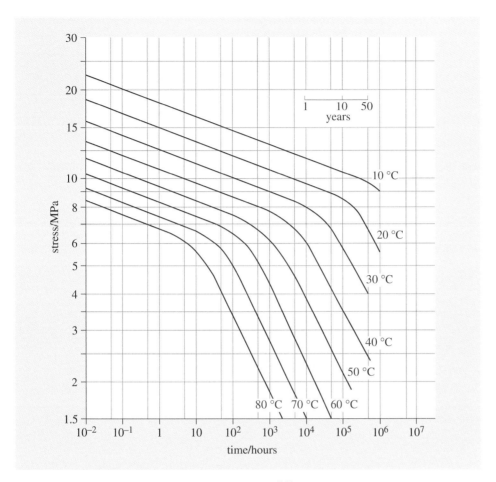

Figure 6.13   Creep rupture data for an HDPE at different temperatures

One important message of this course is that stressed components are liable to contain cracks, and that fracture mechanics should be used to check the design of such products. Therefore, for polyethylene gas pipe, we would be remiss if we did not ascertain the likely size of cracks and flaws, and check whether the conditions were such that these flaws might grow.

For example, *environmental stress cracking* (ESC) is the name used in the plastics industry for the phenomenon called stress corrosion cracking by metallurgists. When it occurs, cracks grow without any large-scale yielding under the combined effect of a tensile stress and some environmental agent. ESC was observed in polyethylene in the earliest applications of the polymer as cable insulation for radar applications. Consequently, a number of empirical tests have been developed to measure the ESC resistance of polyethylene, which is affected by a number of different chemicals including synthetic oils, detergents and alcohols such as methanol. As a result, care needs to be taken when selecting leak-detection fluids, which make soap bubbles when testing joints in polyethylene pipes for leakage.

3.3 Summary

One of the important messages of Block 2 has been that over time, the load-bearing ability of a structure can reduce, leading to failure. Fatigue and corrosion are two mechanisms by which this can occur: creep is another. Creep is often overlooked because of the erroneous assumption that materials properties do not change with temperature. This example is a relatively straightforward one of incorporating creep data into a design specification.

The final case study gives an example of using a material outside its recommended temperature range.

4 FAILURE OF COMPOSITE PRODUCTS

Composite materials made from polymers offer substantial advantages over metals in a wide variety of products, owing to their great resistance to fatigue-crack propagation, their low densities and their generally good chemical resistance. Thus, for example, such materials have completely replaced metal-alloy ☑ **helicopter rotor blades** ☑ because this means that fatigue cracks are effectively eliminated. Thin composite shells can also be constructed to provide aircraft fuselages, wings and other parts of the craft, being well developed in the Airbus series of planes and in the Dreamliner from Boeing.

However, the way in which composite structures are analysed in terms of their fatigue performance is very different from the analysis of metallic structures. In some cases, uncertainty about the way fatigue damage develops and how it can be detected means that metals continue to be used even where highly desirable weight savings are possible: see ☑ **Fatigue of composites** ☑.

☑ Helicopter rotor blades

There were a number of serious accidents in the 1960s and 1970s as a result of fatigue-crack failures of rotor blades on helicopters. Since the rotor blades alone provide lift, acting effectively as wings, their failure results in complete loss of control: the aircraft involved literally fell out of the sky. Cracks grew from tiny defects in the outer surface of the alloy blades, such as surface scratches, under the high bending and centrifugal forces exerted on the blade during take-off, flight and landing. Since the blades were effectively monobloc products (i.e. made in a single casting), there was little to arrest the cracks before catastrophic failure.

By contrast, composite blades developed using high-performance fibres, such as carbon and aramid embedded in an epoxy resin matrix shell around a foam core, offer much better fatigue resistance. (You may recall from Part 4 of this block that aramids are a type of stiff, thermally stable nylon often used in composites to increase modulus and strength.) The blades are made either by machine or by hand lay-up of the composite layers onto the core; this is followed by carefully controlled curing in an oven. A typical rotor-blade structure is shown in Figure 6.14.

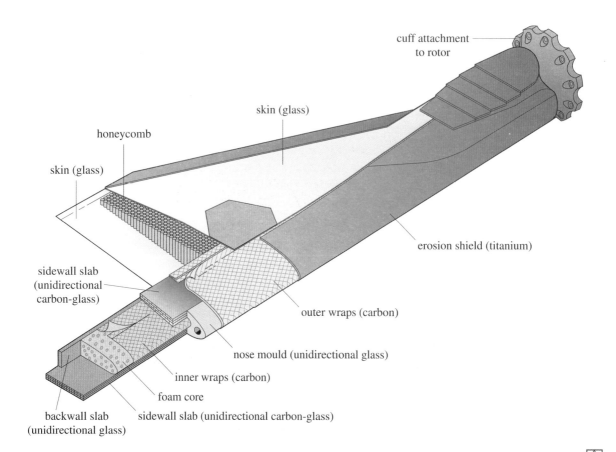

Figure 6.14   Oblique section of helicopter rotor blade, showing construction

▽ Fatigue of composites

Polymer-based composites offer significant challenges to the designer in evaluating and using their fatigue properties. Metals have the distinct advantage that their failure life can be easily measured and well defined in a fatigue test: see for example Figure 6.15, showing a test to failure of an aircraft-wing panel structure.

Composite structures, because of their more complex internal configuration (like the rotor blade shown in Figure 6.14), do not fail in such a clear-cut fashion. There may never be total separation of the component into two pieces. As fatigue cycling continues, there may be extensive delamination and fibre fracture within the component, coupled with a gradual loss of stiffness and strength.

As composite materials are made up of two macroscopic phases, the fibres and the matrix, it is not possible to apply linear-elastic fracture mechanics to them. Cracks can be bridged by fibres in the wake of the crack; and because the material is not isotropic, the stress field is not of the same form as that associated with the K parameter (described back in Part 1 of this block). Instead, approaches based on the amount of strain energy released as the crack advances are used to characterize crack extension in polymer composites. In metals, there is a link between K and the release rate of strain energy, but this is not so for composites; thus small polymer-composite test pieces cannot be used to predict the behaviour of large structures in the same way that metal laboratory samples can.

(b)

(a)

Figure 6.15 Fatigue testing metallic aircraft-wing structures: (a) testing of the structure; (b) failure

Strain-energy methods characterize fracture only for samples of similar geometry and scale. They can be used to provide a material ranking parameter, rather than a quantitative design parameter.

Fatigue-lifing methods based on the Paris law ($\mathrm{d}a/\mathrm{d}N = C(\Delta K)^m$), which are standard for metals and upon which the 'Fatigue calculator' spreadsheet is based, must be modified. A form of the Paris law in which ΔK is replaced by ΔG, the strain-energy release-rate range, has been shown to apply to fatigue delamination crack growth in polymer composites.

Composite materials also have to be used with care if they contain aligned fibres, as their properties will then vary depending on the direction in which a load is experienced.

The effects on residual strength of damage from impacts in service (known in aerospace jargon as *fodding*, from 'foreign object damage') can be worse for composite materials; in particular, damaged components may be far more tricky to repair than the metal equivalent.

But composites do have advantages, which is why they have become widespread in many applications. They offer lower density compared with almost all other structural materials, often at lower cost. Fatigue damage can be allowed without a significant reduction in overall strength, and composites can be stressed elastically at far greater proportions of their ultimate tensile strength than can aluminium alloys. However, the damage they do sustain is not as detectable as a well-behaved Paris-law fatigue crack that can be detected growing in a metallic structure.

4.1 Structure of composite materials

So what is the basis of the great resistance to crack growth of composite materials? All composites consist of a matrix filled with a finely divided material, often in fibre form. The fibres will be chosen on several grounds, including their stiffness, density and cost. Glass fibre is by far the most common fibre in everyday usage – my new bath is a glass-fibre-reinforced polymer – because it is much stiffer than polymer matrices, is relatively cheap and can be produced in a very wide variety of different forms. However, most of the high-performance fibres used in aerospace applications, for example, are usually (although not always) prohibitively expensive for consumer products. They include aramids and carbon fibre: see ☑ **High-performance fibres** ☑.

☑ High-performance fibres

Glass is just one option today for fibre reinforcement of composite structures. There are many new polymers with very high tensile moduli and strengths that have been used in structures, starting with carbon fibre (developed in the 1950s) and continuing up to the aramid fibres such as Kevlar® and Twaron® (developed in the 1960s). More recent fibres include Spectra® and Dyneema®, which are based on ultra-high molecular weight polyethylene (UHMWPE) and were developed in the 1980s and 1990s.

Applications of these fibres are numerous, especially where structural integrity is of prime concern – as in rotor vanes and propellers, where their resistance to fatigue is combined with a low overall weight and good resistance to corrosion. Such fibres are also widely used in lightweight shells in many different forms of vehicle, including aircraft (in wings, tails and fuselages), yachts, racing sculls, racing cars, racing bikes and so on. Very long, thin tubes serve as masts or, on a smaller scale, in more everyday products such as fishing rods.

The properties that can be attained are impressive: unidirectional carbon fibre in an epoxy matrix, for example, has a tensile modulus of 200 GPa (similar to steel) and a strength of 1400 MPa (competing with the best high-strength steels).

The properties of the different fibres (density ρ, Young's modulus E and tensile strength σ_{TS}) are shown in Table 6.1. Aramids are available in several grades of varying strength and find use in many different guises, such as body armour and other forms of ballistic protection. Like carbon fibre, aramid is temperature-resistant up to 420 °C, so also provides fire protection. One unusual application involves very short fibres or fluff in an epoxy matrix for brake pads, where it has replaced asbestos fibres. Dyneema is the most recent high-performance fibre; since it is a form of UHMWPE, it has a very high strength. This is why the material is used for prosthetic hip-joint sockets, where its high abrasion and fatigue resistance are highly prized attributes.

Table 6.1   Properties of different high-performance fibres

Fibre		$\rho/$ kg m^{-3}	$E/$ GN m^{-2}	$\sigma_{TS}/$ GN m^{-2}	$E\rho^{-1}/$ MN m kg^{-1}	$\sigma_{TS}\rho^{-1}/$ MN m kg^{-1}
Aramid	Kevlar 29	1400	60	2.8	42.9	2.00
	Kevlar 49	1440	124	3.1	86.1	2.15
UHMWPE (polyethylene)	Spectra 900	970	120	2.6	124	2.68
Polypropylene	gel-spun	910	36	1.0	39.6	1.10
Carbon fibre*	UHM	1960	520	1.9	265	0.97
	HM	1850	480	2.0	259	1.08
	UHS	1750	270	5.2	154	2.97
	HS	1760	265	2.8	151	1.59
Steel piano wire		7860	210	3.0	26.7	0.38

* (U)HM: (ultra) high modulus; (U)HS: (ultra) high strength

Since the interface between the matrix and the fibre is critical to the strength of the final product, it is important to choose the combination carefully. For instance, polyethylene fibres will not bond easily to a normal thermoset resin matrix, so composites of Dyneema and epoxy show a low strength owing to the lack of good bonding. Such fibres are better suited to ropes and cables, where they have become dominant for their good corrosion resistance and very high strength and stiffness-to-weight ratio. So, heavy-duty plaited cables made from Dyneema are now normal for mooring supertankers, for example, owing to the combination of a density less than water (so the rope floats) and very high strength, to resist movement of the ship.

However, failures have occurred with high-performance cables, as the following case study describes.

Case study: failure of a mooring cable

The use of aramid cables for mooring large ships was tried for the first time in 1983 in the Gulf of

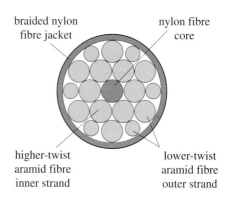

Figure 6.16   Structure of the mooring lines

Mexico, where the construction derrick ship *Ocean Builder* was being used to build an oil-drilling tower. Twelve lines were used to moor it in seawater 300 m deep, each line being 60 mm in diameter and constructed from aramid cables around a nylon core (Figure 6.16). Each line was anchored at the seabed by a steel chain, and a further steel cable was used to anchor the ship directly (Figure 6.17).

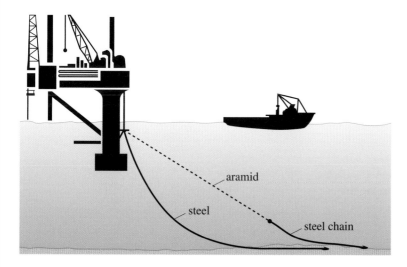

Figure 6.17   Mooring of the *Ocean Builder*

On first tensioning the system, four to six weeks after deployment, four of the aramid cables parted at a fifth of their rated strength of 200 tonnes (the rated strength of a rope or cable is the maximum load that it is able to bear). When the cables were disassembled, extensive kinking of single filaments of the aramid fibres was found (Figure 6.18a).

Kinks such as those shown in the figure form at 0.5 to 0.8% compressive strain. Tests on new cable after the failure showed that only about 10 compressive cycles were needed to form kink bands. Once formed, they acted as a hinge about which further fatigue could occur when strained cyclically.

So how did the repetitive strain occur in the first place? It was essentially tide and wave motion in the Gulf that caused the cables to twist up and unwind cyclically. When twisted up too tightly, the fibres were compressed and formed the kink bands. Low-load fatigue thus caused fibre fracture and failure of the cables. During the unwinding part of the cycle, the braided nylon fibre jacket eventually split, forming a 'birdcage' in the cable (Figure 6.18b). The wetted cables were also found to be more susceptible to fatigue than when they were dry.

The main recommendations of the failure analysis were to change the mode of construction from hawser (where the strands are twisted together to form the line) to braided or even straight-aligned fibres, and to use a solid sheath of extruded plastic to prevent water ingress.

In fact, use of aramid in this application has been discontinued in favour of the conventional practice of using steel cables or chains. However, the use

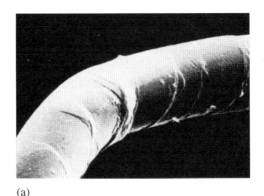

(a)

(b)

Figure 6.18   (a) Kinked aramid fibre; (b) 'birdcage' formed in aramid cable

of polyethylene cables has increased in marine applications owing to their greater strength-to-weight ratio, resistance to degradation from sunlight and water, and very low inherent density, allowing them to float freely if released.

As long as the aramid cables are freely suspended, and unlikely to be compressed, then they can be used to replace conventional tethers, such as stays for radio and TV masts, optical cable transmission lines and supports for electrical transmission lines (on tramways, for example). They can replace galvanized steel cable as well as conventional fibre rope such as nylon or polyester.

4.1.1 Glass-reinforced plastic

Glass-reinforced plastic (GRP) consists of a matrix made from one of various thermoset polymers, with any one of a number of possible glass-fibre fillers. Glass fibre has a much higher stiffness than the matrix material; thus when mixed, the resulting composite is much stiffer than the matrix alone. It is also much tougher, simply because cracks cannot normally grow easily across fibres: they are forced to travel along the weak interface between the fibre and the matrix, so increasing the net energy needed to fracture the composite product.

The two most common plastic matrices are polyester or epoxy resins. Both are brittle with a low tensile modulus (it being the glass fibre that adds stiffness). Polyester is a cheaper matrix than epoxy, and is usually the easiest to use during manufacture. In fact, polyester is so easy to use, requiring simple mixing of the resin with a cross-linking agent just before use, that there is a popular market for such materials in DIY applications. However, epoxy resin is in fact the better matrix, because it has a higher resistance to heat than polyester.

4.1.2 Applications of glass-reinforced plastic

GRP has been widely used for a number of years in many common products, including car-body shells, corrugated roof sheeting and small boat hulls (canoes and dinghies, for example). Indeed, it may be used anywhere that light, thin-walled shells can replace heavy metal components, saving weight and frequently manufacturing costs as well. Manufacturing methods vary from the most primitive (hand lay-up) to automated application of the materials. Hand lay-up is, of course, highly labour-intensive, and so is applicable only to small production runs.

Figure 6.19 shows an example of a much larger-scale application of GRP in boat hulls. Here the hull needs to be non-magnetic, and very tough in order to resist sub-sea explosions. The figure shows a *Hunt* class mine countermeasures vessel (MCMV), one of 13 similar ships (the first of which, HMS *Brecon*, was launched in 1978). These ships have been used in active roles in the Falklands campaign and the Gulf War, as well as acting as fishery protection vessels. In such structures, maximum strength is obtained when layers of woven glass rovings (lightly twisted fibres) are used as reinforcement (Figure 6.20a). The hull typically uses up to 40 such layers at its thickest part, with a polyester resin matrix (Figure 6.20b).

There are many other vessels worldwide that exploit GRP in hull structures, mainly for the freedom it allows in shaping the hull, together with its resistance to corrosion. However, it is more expensive than steel owing to the necessarily slow process of building the structure layer by layer, usually by hand. The process cannot be speeded up easily because heat is given out during polymerization of the polyester or epoxy matrix, and this heat must be dissipated before the next layer is applied. A similar problem occurs in building large structures, such as dam walls, with cement and concrete.

Figure 6.19 A *Hunt* class MCMV

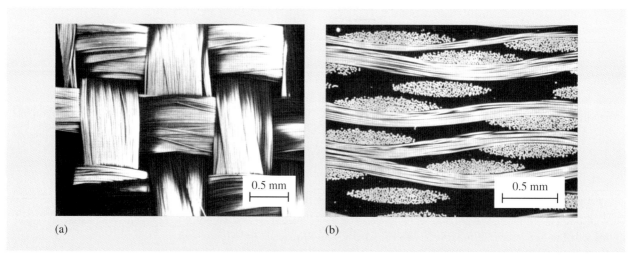

Figure 6.20 (a) Scanning electron microscope (SEM) image of woven glass rovings without resin applied; (b) section through composite, taken using an optical microscope

GRP has also been applied to the mass manufacture of car bodies – such as that of the Renault Espace, for example. Such methods demand very large capital investment in machines large and powerful enough to inject very viscous mixtures into steel moulds. However, the resulting lower weight compared with a steel body improves performance, and the material is resistant to corrosion. Speciality models, such as sports and racing cars, exploit composite body shells by using high-performance fibres, usually in an epoxy resin matrix. They have improved the survival rate of car rally drivers enormously, the shell being designed to absorb the high impact loads of a high-speed crash so as to shield the driver. The expense of the materials, however, precludes their widespread application to mass-production cars.

4.2 Storage tanks

4.2.1 Choice of materials

Thermosetting polymers have a 'fixed', highly cross-linked chain structure after fabrication, so they cannot be re-formed. Araldite® is an example of a thermoset epoxy. On the other hand, thermoplastics can be softened and reprocessed, as the polymer chains can still have mobility.

Glass-fibre-reinforced thermosets have been widely used to make storage tanks for many years and compete effectively with steel structures, at least for smaller tank sizes (with fluid capacity of up to several hundred tonnes). An alternative is to use completely thermoplastic tanks, which are much easier to fabricate, involving simply bending large, flat extruded sheet into a cylinder and then welding the edges together to form the final structure. The resistance of many thermoplastics to chemicals is high, so they are increasingly used for chemical storage. Polyethylene and polypropylene are two low-cost materials that are used widely, owing to their ease of shaping and their resistance to many chemicals.

However, the apparent advantage of thermoplastic tanks may be eliminated unless they are designed correctly. Such design needs careful thought, in order to provide sufficient thickness of material in the tank wall to resist hydrostatic pressure from the contents when the tank is full. When this is not achieved, failure can result, as ▽ **Catastrophic rupture of a thermoplastic tank** ▽ shows.

☑ Catastrophic rupture of a thermoplastic tank

The use of thermoplastic tanks is widespread both in the chemical industry and in industries that make use of chemicals in the manufacture of other products. They are frequently made of sheet polypropylene, bent into shape and welded thermally to produce the final cylindrical shape. Tanks up to about 100 tonnes in capacity use 12 mm extruded flat-sheet polymer. However, the wall thickness needs careful consideration, since the walls must resist the large hoop stresses at and near the bottom of such tanks.

In the mid-1990s, one such tank with a wall thickness of 12 mm and a diameter of 2.7 m suddenly ruptured, spewing a 40% caustic soda solution over the bund wall into the surrounding factory (a bund is an outer wall around a tank that is intended to act as protective containment if the inner wall fails). The corrosive fluid caused half a million pounds' worth of damage to the factory and adjacent property in Warrington, but fortunately no one was injured.

The rupture occurred on the night shift, some hours after a full load of caustic soda had been delivered to the factory and stored in the tank. It was the fourth full load to have been stored in that particular tank since installation.

The structure of the tank is shown in Figure 6.21, together with the position of the failure, showing the exit of a jet of fluid from a crack in the tank. This crack occurred at a vertical weld just under halfway up the tank, and the panel in which it occurred showed some outward bulging (Figure 6.22). The deformation visible in the figure is permanent, since the tank was empty at the time the photograph was taken. The crack was found to be at the centre of the weld (marked by the large arrow in Figure 6.22).

The bulging of the tank visible in Figure 6.22 (tilt the page to see the distortion more clearly, or put a ruler against the vertical weld) is evidence of creep: the polymer has bent out of shape owing to the internal hydrostatic pressure when the tank was full. As mentioned in Section 3, creep typically occurs above $0.4T_{\mathrm{m}}$, where T_{m} is the melting point of the material in kelvin. Thus although it tends to occur at elevated temperatures, for some polymers the ambient room temperature may be high enough to activate creep processes.

Since a storage tank is effectively a type of pressure vessel, the formulae we developed in Block 1 Part 4 can be applied (while recognizing that pressure varies from point to point in a tank, rather than being constant, because the pressure will be greater at the bottom of the tank than at the top). The hoop stress in the tank, σ_{h}, may be calculated using the formula:

$$\sigma_{\mathrm{h}} = pr/t$$

where p is the hydrostatic pressure at any point, r is the radius of the tank and t is the wall thickness.

The pressure in the tank can be evaluated using the equation:

$$p = h\rho g$$

where h is the depth from the top of the fluid, ρ is the density of the fluid and g is the acceleration due to gravity. Given that the caustic soda had

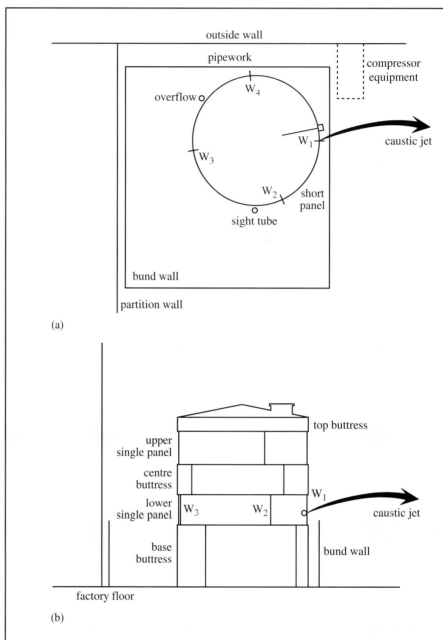

Figure 6.21 (a) Top-down and (b) side-on view of the location and geometry of the failed tank: the labels W_1–W_4 mark the positions of the vertical welds in the relevant section of the tank

a density of 1500 kg m^{-3} and that the crack was 2 m below the highest fluid level, then:

$$p = 2 \text{ m} \times 1500 \text{ kg m}^{-3} \times 9.81 \text{ m s}^{-2} = 29.4 \text{ kPa}$$

So:

$$\sigma_h = (29.4 \text{ kPa} \times 1.35 \text{ m})/0.012 \text{ m} = 3.4 \text{ MPa}$$

Tensile tests on some specimen welds showed a mean strength of about 21 MPa, with an error of ±1 MPa, so why had the panel failed? The

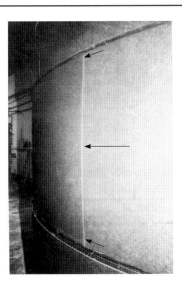

Figure 6.22   Location of the failure

strength of the weld should be quite sufficient to withstand a small hoop stress of only 3.4 MPa.

Thermal welds in polypropylene are formed by bending the two free edges of a long sheet together, then heating the two edges and holding them together under load. The weld can be weakened by holes where the polymer has not fused, which is why welds are tested. The defect in this case was just such a hole, as the fracture surface showed (Figure 6.23). The small hole produced a stress concentration of 4 to 5, so the crack started at the base of the hole when the tank was full.

The defect grew when the tank was fully filled for the first time (1), and so on (2–3) until at the fourth full load (4) the crack had nearly crossed the wall. After that, only a small amount of slow crack growth was needed to cause rupture.

In a follow-up inspection of the way the tank was made, it was found that the panels were bent around to form the cylinders, which were then stacked up to create the tank. This meant that each panel was stressed, causing the outer side to be in a state of uniform tension. This tension was estimated at 1.5–1.8 MPa. Adding this to the stress calculated above means that the total hoop stress at the fracture point will thus have been 4.9–5.2 MPa, and the weld defect will have increased this locally.

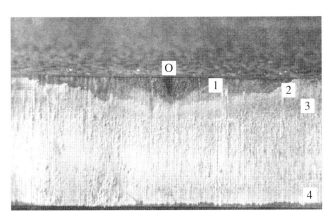

Figure 6.23
Fracture surface showing origin of the defect and its growth stages

Construction of the tank violated numerous recommendations of the relevant standard, DVS 2205, a standard from the German Welding Institute dated 1987. The wall thickness, although nominally adequate, was less than that recommended by the standard (Figure 6.24).

The tank had been under-designed: the wall should have been increased in thickness at the bottom of the tank to resist the linear increase in pressure with depth.

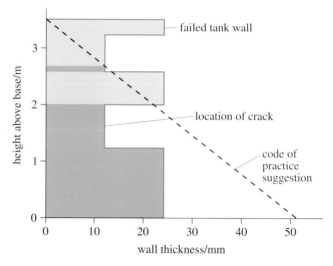

Figure 6.24 Actual wall-thickness profile compared with the requirements of the relevant standard. The darker green areas show the regions where the thickness of the tank wall was less than that suggested by the code of practice

Welds are always weaker than parent material, so can be a problem in achieving a strong product. Polymer welds are often tested using a spark 'gun', but the method detects only through-thickness holes and not partial holes. Such holes can act as serious stress raisers, as in the case of the Warrington tank. However, tiny defects of this kind are normally irrelevant, because a good design should allow for such inevitable problems by employing an appropriate safety factor.

Glass reinforcement offers much stiffer walls than thermoplastic materials alone, with the necessary toughness to limit crack growth as well. The most common arrangement of glass fibre and resin matrix used in GRPs is chopped strand mat (CSM), which consists of a mat of short glass fibres randomly arrayed in flat sheets and impregnated with the fluid resin to form the final shape. However, CSM is also the weakest of the many possible alternatives, since the fibres are randomly oriented in the plane of each layer; as a direct result, its strength is low (55–117 MPa). Much stronger GRP materials are available for building large storage tanks, but their cost is also higher. For example, using woven cloth as the reinforcing agent means that the weave of the fabric can be oriented to resist the hoop stress, giving a higher strength of approximately 200 MPa. The best option of all is unidirectional glass fibre, in which all the fibres can be aligned against the hoop stress; this uniform orientation gives it a strength of around 700 MPa. Its manufacture requires special equipment to wind the fibre in a spiral form to make the walls, but it gives the safest structure.

Reinforced tanks are frequently lined with thermoplastics for the chemical resistance those materials offer. In such cases, the liner is manufactured first and then used as the template on which the GRP outer shell can be built.

4.2.2 Mechanisms of failure

Clearly, tank rupture can have extremely serious consequences, especially if the contents are highly corrosive or toxic (or both), and every user should be aware of the risks. There are several conceivable failure modes, including slow leakage from small wall defects and, at the other end of the scale, catastrophic failure when the most highly stressed part, the wall, suddenly fails and releases the contents in a destructive wave. Since the wall stress is highest when the tank is full, failure is most likely then, as the case of the Warrington tank showed. The likely damage rises with the absolute size of the tank, as you might expect, since the sheer volume of fluid released increases with size. The maximum hoop stress depends on the height and density of the fluid contained in the tank, so there are design compromises that need to be made when assembling storage tanks into plant.

The nature of the contained fluid is also important for assessing the kind of damage caused. Thus water, by far the most common stored fluid, will usually cause extensive physical damage but little chemical damage to its surroundings. However, if water-sensitive products such as books, paper and textiles are nearby then the damage may be severe.

Analysing the nature of the stresses in products is the first step in attempting to determine the cause of failure. With cylindrical storage tanks, the matter is simplified by knowing that when the wall is thin compared with the overall diameter, the hoop stress σ_h acting along the circumference is twice the longitudinal (axial) stress σ_a acting along the length of the tank. The material of which the wall is made is irrelevant to this calculation; naturally, however, steel is the most widely used wall material for larger tanks in industry, being a common sight at tank farms where products like oil and petrol are stored. There have been some spectacular disasters caused by wall failure in steel tanks, such as ☑ the Boston molasses-tank failure ☑.

☑ The Boston molasses-tank failure

That tank rupture can occur for any wall material is shown by the catastrophic rupture of a very large tank in Boston in 1919. The tank was located on the dockside near the present centre of the city, and caused widespread damage when it ruptured on 17 January. The failure killed 21 dock workers and other locals. A map of the tank's surroundings and the location of the physical damage is shown in Figure 6.25.

The tank stood nearly 15 m high and at the time of failure had just been filled with 8.7 million litres of molasses, a viscous sugar used for making industrial alcohol. The tank had been filled to capacity just seven times in its two-year life. Investigation of the remains showed that the tank had failed by brittle cracking from the edge of a manhole near the base of the tank. The hole was on the south-west side of the tank, so the most severe damage was seen on the adjacent elevated railway and nearby buildings. The tank was built using 17 mm thick steel at the base, from plates riveted together.

Two theories to explain the failure were proposed. There had been a series of bomb

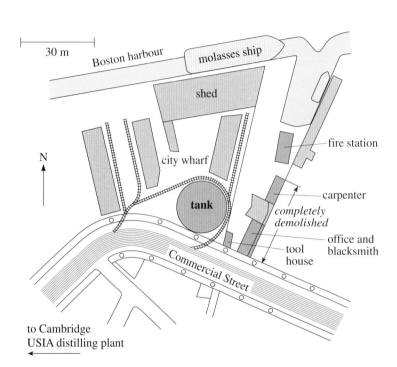

Figure 6.25   Location of the tank and the resulting damage

attacks by anarchists in other US cities, so it was thought that a bomb placed at the base could have caused the failure. However, while a small bomb could have been placed easily at the base of the tank, the absence of shattered glass windows in buildings close to the centre of a possible blast argued against a detonation. The alternative explanation was that the structure was faulty and had been under-designed. Such structural failure was more likely, and was supported by a number of facts:

- The tank had not been tested before use, by filling it with water so that any distortion or leakage could be detected.

- Many leaks had occurred after recent fills, enabling local residents to collect seepage for their own use.

- The fracture was entirely brittle and occurred at the edge of a 0.6 m diameter circular manhole, a well-known stress concentrator.

- The weather at the time of the failure was not cold, and the molasses was warm owing to natural fermentation occurring in the fluid.

SAQ 6.8 (Learning outcome 6.4)

Estimate the stress at the base of the tank when full of molasses of density 1500 kg m^{-3}. You will first need to estimate the diameter of the tank from Figure 6.25.

Discuss possible failure mechanisms in the light of your analysis and other information on the structure of the tank. (Assume that the tensile strength of steel is about 1100 MPa.)

Hint: consider the stress concentrations near the location of the fracture.

The affair went to a civil trial in the courts, where it was eventually decided in favour of the many victims. The court found that the tank had been untested, that it had been built by an unqualified engineer, and that the design had not been checked independently by another engineer.

Figure 6.26   Failed dairy tank (made from GRP with a polypropylene liner)

So, catastrophic rupture of a tank wall can occur through several mechanisms, including under-design as well as effects such as stress corrosion cracking and poor fabrication. Sometimes, catastrophic failure can occur years after installation and use, as when a dairy silo suddenly collapsed after 10 years in service (Figure 6.26). This failure occurred because the slightly acidic contents leaked through the liner, causing stress corrosion cracking at a repaired weld near the base of the silo.

SAQ 6.9 (Learning outcomes 6.3 and 6.4, and Block 1 revision)

In a typical tank structure, sheet material will be welded using a combination of horizontal and vertical welds to produce the final shape. Which welds are the most critical?

Especial care is thus needed for finished welds, which is why most tank standards specify intensive non-destructive testing of the final structure. Any defects in the weld (such as gaps or holes) will act as stress concentrators, and thus will be the most likely spots where brittle cracks may start. Fatigue caused by regular filling and emptying is an obvious failure mechanism for tanks with defective welds. Degradation of the GRP shell can also occur over a longer timeframe if leaks develop in the liner, as the example of the dairy silo showed. Polyester is susceptible to hydrolysis from acidic residues, so stress corrosion cracking is a possible failure mechanism in the case of a small internal leak. Such a problem is very difficult to detect, since the critical crack is concealed from view.

4.3 Tank failure case study

Given the well-known cases of catastrophic failure of large tanks, it is rather surprising to learn that such failures continue to occur. But just such a failure took place as recently as 2003, when a 100-tonne storage tank at a chemical works on Teesside suddenly failed, releasing its contents into the plant and destroying much nearby equipment. The subsequent insurance claim was in excess of a quarter of a million pounds. Fortunately no one was injured, since the plant was actually operated by very few personnel.

According to evidence from the site managers, the tank had been full at the time of failure, so was under maximum pressure from the contents. In addition, it appeared that the contents could have been very hot, possibly up to a temperature of 90 °C.

The initial investigation concluded that the tank had been under-designed for its purpose and had probably failed from an outlet pipe near the base. However, the failure was then reinvestigated by the insurers, since the initial study had been conducted for the plant managers, who had a vested interest in the outcome. Although the first investigation had been conducted by a reputable body outside the company concerned, there could have been evidence or circumstances that were not considered but that were relevant to the failure.

4.3.1 Reinvestigation of the failure

Reinvestigation inevitably involved reinspection of the remains of the tank, which fortunately had been kept for just this purpose. The key piece of evidence was the set of parts at and near the inferred initiation zone at the outlet pipe, consisting of the main wall with outlet pipe and a fragment of the integral bund wall nearby.

Photographs of the failed tank were also made available, showing the extent of the damage (Figure 6.27a). The bund wall had clearly itself failed after the rupture of the main sidewall of the inner tank (Figure 6.27b). Figure 6.27(c) shows the remains

(a)

(b)

(c)

Figure 6.27   (a) and (b) The failed tank (only the collapsed bund wall is visible); (c) the base of the tank

after they were stripped and piled elsewhere: the base of the tank is visible in the foreground of the photograph, clearly showing the thicker inner part of the base where the inner tank was situated, and the narrow outer region between the bund and the tank itself.

Whatever event had initiated the final catastrophic failure, it appeared to have occurred on just one side of the structure, and caused extensive brittle fracture of both the outer bund wall and the inner wall of the tank. The tank showed complete brittle fractures to the outer bund wall, concentrated at the lower outer sides (right-hand side of Figure 6.27a). Figure 6.27(a) also shows partial brittle fractures at lower left, near a circular cut-out, and ductile deformation of the steel frame.

4.3.2 Tank specification

The next step in the process was to examine the specification of the tank, including not just the physical structure of the finished tank but also the conditions under which it would operate. The aim of this task was ultimately to compare the proposed design and reality, to see whether there were any discrepancies.

Figure 6.28 shows a plan of the equipment surrounding the tank. It can be seen that the tank was part of a complicated chemical process in which a catalyst was polished using alternate acidic and alkaline washes. The tank acted as a reservoir for the effluent produced during these treatments, so would have contained a mixture of

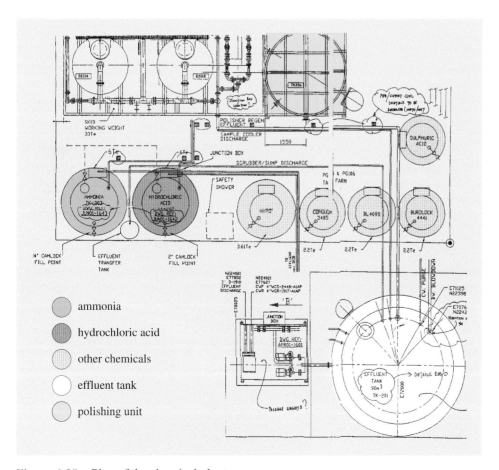

Figure 6.28   Plan of the chemical plant

different aqueous solutions, the exact composition depending on processing of the catalyst.

Figure 6.29 shows a section through the tank and bund, giving the overall dimensions of the structure. The bund wall was supported by a steel frame, and there was an inspection ladder fitted at one side of the tank (Figure 6.27a).

Celmar is polypropylene sheet laminated with polyester. A glass-reinforced resin is then applied to the polyester backing: in this case, chopped strand mat (CSM) was used.

According to the specification, the liner should have been polypropylene of 6 mm thickness, with a reinforcing shell consisting of six layers of Celmar® GRP, each layer being 1.5 mm thick. This gave a total shell thickness of 9 mm and, thus, a total wall thickness of 15 mm. The bund wall was specified to be of identical construction. The tank should have weighed 4 tonnes, and been able to support a static load of 104 tonnes from the contents at a temperature of 90 °C.

The specification also stated that the tank should be a Category III design according to a 1987 British Standard (BS 4994). What this means is explained in Table 6.2.

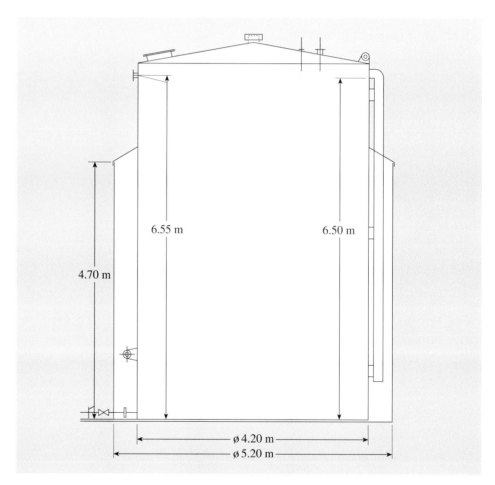

6.55 m   6.50 m

4.70 m

ø 4.20 m

ø 5.20 m

Figure 6.29   Tank section

Table 6.2   Minimum categories of vessel or tank, taken from BS 4994

	Category I	Category II	Category III
Contents*			
Toxic	X		
Highly corrosive	X		
Corrosive			X
Flammable	X		
Others			X
Chemical compatibility of liner with process fluid			
Known long-term compatibility based on service experience			X
Compatibility based on related performance data		X	
Only specimen data (dip coupons) available	X		
Design temperature, T			
$T < 60\ °C$ and $T \le (HDT^{\dagger} - 40\ °C)$			X
$T \ge 60\ °C$ and $T \le (HDT - 40\ °C)$		X	
$T > (HDT - 40\ °C)$ and $T \le (HDT - 20\ °C)$	X		
Design pressure and/or vacuum			
Static head only			X
$< \pm 5$ mbar‡ (above static head)		X	
$\ge \pm 5$ mbar (above static head)	X		
Size of vessel or tank (capacity)			
$< 10\ m^3$			X
$10\ m^3 \le$ capacity $\le 50\ m^3$		X	
$> 50\ m^3$	X		
Geometry and supports			
Flat bottom, full support			X
Any other, e.g. legs, skirts, saddles, rings and frames		X	
Other criteria			
If item is critical to safety	X		

*Description of contents classification
Toxic: the contents could present a significant risk to health of persons exposed.
Highly corrosive: the contents could severely burn, blind, disfigure or maim an individual.
Corrosive: the contents could cause damage to the skin or eye.
Flammable: the contents have a flash point equal to or less than 55 °C.
Others: the contents are not considered to burn, blind or injure individuals.

†Heat distortion temperature of resin.

‡1 mbar = 100 N m^{-2} = 100 Pa.

SAQ 6.10 (Learning outcome 6.6)

Using the criteria shown in Table 6.2, determine the category of the tank by matching the design specification shown in Figures 6.28 and 6.29 with the relevant properties in the table. Was the tank assigned the correct category in the specification?

4.3.3 Dimensions of the wall

Large fragments of the tank were available for examination, so an obvious first step was to section and measure the walls at various critical points in the structure. Figure 6.30 shows a section through the base of the tank. Here, the upper part is the 6 mm thick inner liner of polypropylene, which has a smooth, featureless surface. The lower part of the section is the laminated GRP outer shell, which is of somewhat greater thickness than the inner liner.

EXERCISE 6.4

Use the scale bar to estimate the range of thickness of the composite outer shell across the section shown in Figure 6.30. How many layers are there at each part of the section, if each layer is 1.5 mm thick?

So, at least at some points on the section, the number of GRP layers appears to meet the specification: six layers, each 1.5 mm in thickness. However, the section decreases in thickness towards the corner where the base meets the vertical wall of the tank. Here, as the answer to Exercise 6.4 showed, the number of layers is lower than specified, i.e. only five. Indeed, it can be seen in Figure 6.30 that one of the layers on the right-hand side tapers off before it reaches the corner.

Figure 6.30   Section through the tank base

The vertical wall is shown in section in Figure 6.31. This time, knowing that the inner liner is 6 mm thick suggests an outer shell thickness of just under 7 mm – this being reasonably uniform across the section visible in the figure – which means that the outer composite shell must be between four and five layers in thickness. Since it isn't possible to have a fraction of a layer, one reason for the discrepancy might be that a so-called gel coat has been added on the outside, in which case the actual number of layers must be only four rather than the specified six. Gel-coat outer layers are not reinforced, so provide little extra strength to the wall.

The final photograph of the cut sections from the tank (Figure 6.32) shows the corner fracture, already seen in section in the previous figures, in the foreground. The inner thermoplastic liner is at the top, together with the remains of a weld just behind the corner fracture. The broken surface of the corner shows a typical composite fracture with individual glass fibres exposed by multiple crack growth. In addition, the two arrows in the figure mark the remnants of some aluminium foil that must have been used for testing the weld. Such remains are normally removed at the end of weld testing, and may have weakened the junction at the corner.

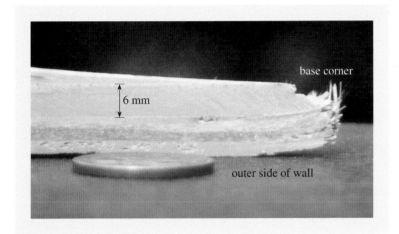

Figure 6.31 Wall section near the base corner

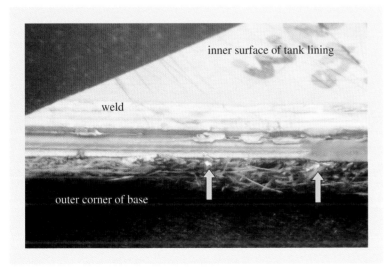

Figure 6.32 View of corner fracture showing foil fragments: the aluminium foil is placed behind the weld when using a spark tester for leaks, and should have been removed after testing rather than remaining in place

4.3.4 Reassembly of the parts

One important way of assessing catastrophic ruptures is to reassemble the key parts to see how their final states relate to one another. The broken parts are shown in Figure 6.33, aligned roughly as they would have been in service. The critical fracture occurred at a pipe connection to the tank, through which fluid could be drained away into an effluent stream. Such a pipe must have required two circular holes in the tank structure, one in the bund and the other in the tank wall. So what does the reassembly show?

The most striking feature is the vertical curvature visible in the tank wall (centre of the figure: the curvature is most obvious at the far edge of the wall fragment). This can be judged by comparing it with the straight section of the bund wall (left), which was never exposed to continuous load from the fluid contents. The effect was assessed by drawing lines from top to bottom on the inner side of the wall (as shown in greater detail in Figure 6.34), then measuring their displacement from a straight

Figure 6.33
Reassembling the failed parts

Figure 6.34   The curvature in the wall of the main tank

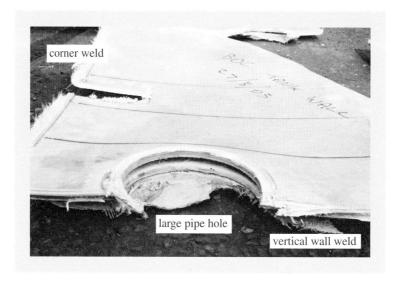

edge placed across the wall. The maximum displacement was 2.3 mm along the greatest height of the wall section (about 1.3 m). Overall, the wall appears to bulge outwards uniformly from the base of the tank, although it is interesting to observe that the region around the pipe hole has resisted the general deformation, presumably owing to the presence of the pipe buttressing the wall.

This curvature of the wall was certainly not in the original specification, and can only have been caused by creep, presumably under the high load imposed by the contents when the tank was full. The phenomenon gave a very clear indication of the events preceding the final failure, because creep in composite materials can occur only if the part in question has been either overloaded on a regular basis or under-designed for the maximum load it had to support. These two possibilities are not mutually exclusive, of course, because if the tank was under-designed then it follows that the walls would have been overloaded when the tank was full of its fluid contents. On the other hand, it might have been filled with a fluid of greater density than had been anticipated, meaning that the pressure inside the tank would be higher. However, this possibility should have been accounted for by incorporating a reasonable safety factor into the design.

SAQ 6.11 (Learning outcomes 6.3 and 6.4)

Calculate the hoop stress in the tank wall when the tank is full. Compare this value with the tensile strength of the CSM used in the outer shell, which is between 55 and 117 MPa at 25 °C, depending on its quality. What is the safety factor?

You will need to calculate the density of the tank contents, which you can do by using the tank dimensions and the maximum design weight of the contents (104 tonnes). Assume that the much greater stiffness of the shell compared to the liner means that the liner can be ignored for the purposes of calculating the hoop stress, and take the thickness of the shell to be the 9 mm specified by the design.

Another important feature that can be seen from Figure 6.34 is the way in which the wall itself has become delaminated. A large gap has formed between the polypropylene liner and the composite layers of the outer shell, presumably a process associated with the distortion discussed already. The problem is most severe around the pipe exit: the cavity formed here was measured to be up to 200 mm deep, extending all around the junction. The corresponding inner surfaces were relatively smooth, suggesting a low energy of adhesion between the polypropylene and the first layer of GRP to be applied during initial construction.

4.3.5 Fracture surface

The fracture surface itself comprised several parts, at and surrounding the pipe outlet (much of which is visible in the foreground of Figure 6.34). The damage here is so extensive as to make identification of the origin impossible. Failure of composites is often much more complicated than failure of homogeneous materials, making the fracture surfaces of less use in determining crack initiation and growth behaviour. The basic reason is that cracks frequently propagate along the fibre–matrix interface, so producing a very complicated crack path.

Figure 6.35 Close-up of failed wall at inlet pipe

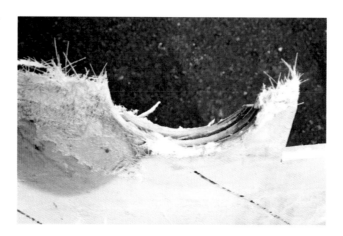

Figure 6.36 Reassembly of the tank wall at the failure point: the inner surface of the wall is shown facing upwards

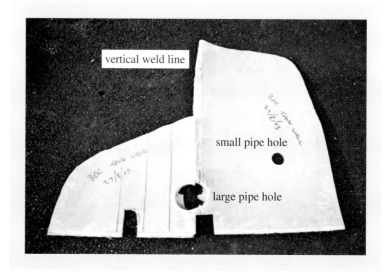

At one point the cracks had grown laterally, exposing a free layer of CSM (Figure 6.35). The exposure shows the random orientation of the glass fibres as they are situated in a single layer.

Figure 6.36 shows two parts of the lower wall laid together, the part on the left being the section shown in close-up in Figure 6.34. It can be seen that there was a smaller pipe hole above and to the right of the larger hole. The critical crack probably started in the region of the lower hole, then grew along the join at which the two sections of polypropylene liner were welded together. Although the small hole would have had a similar stress-raising effect to that of the large hole, it lies somewhat higher from the base and so the hoop stress would have been slightly smaller at that point.

4.3.6 Tank fill history

It was essential to determine over what period the tank had been used since its construction, and how it had been used in conjunction with the output of the catalyst-polishing unit of the plant. Key pieces of information for the investigation were the degree of fill and the temperature of the contents of the tank over its lifetime, together with any other relevant details.

The records of the company running the polishing unit were obtained, and produced the fill and temperature history shown graphically in Figure 6.37. The upper curve is related to the left-hand axis of Figure 6.37, which shows the degree of fill of the tank as a percentage of its total capacity; the lower curve is related to the right-hand axis, which shows the temperature of the contents (as judged by the temperature of the outlet stream from the base of the tank). Since the temperature of the contents was not measured directly, it could have been somewhat higher than that of the outlet stream, especially when the acid and alkali effluents were mixed and thus could have reacted chemically. The levels of acidity or alkalinity (not shown in the figure) were also recorded: they varied from very acidic to highly alkaline, corresponding to usage of the tank to mix varying effluent streams from the polishing unit.

So what does Figure 6.37 show? The tank was always used to at least 70% of its capacity, so the walls were always under hydrostatic load. There were four occasions when it was completely full, thus putting the lower walls under the maximum hoop stress, and about seven further occasions when it was filled to at least 90% of capacity. The temperature of the contents always lay above 80 °C, apart from during several periods in the early life of the tank, when the temperature fell to the ambient temperature of about 20 °C. These presumably occurred when the chemical process was out of action. The very final points reveal that the tank was nearly full at the time of failure and that the temperature of the contents was 90 °C.

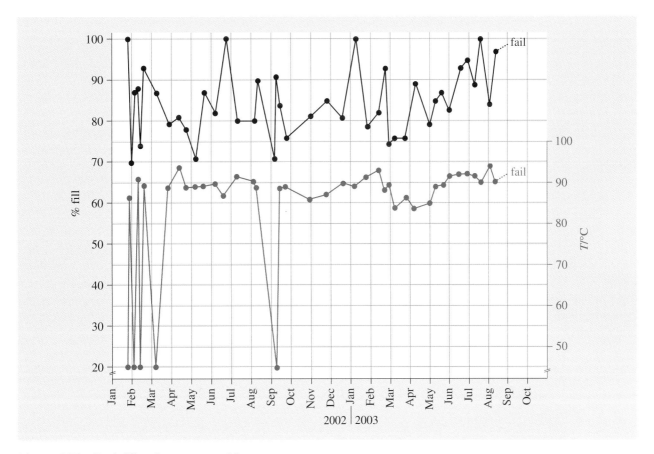

Figure 6.37 Tank fill and temperature history

4.3.7 Materials behaviour

Given the high temperatures to which the tank was exposed, it was important to determine whether the materials of construction (the polypropylene liner and the GRP shell) were capable of resisting those temperatures. The test used to examine the materials was a method known as differential scanning calorimetry (DSC), which involves heating a small sample up at a slow and controlled rate. Any heat flow between the sample and the environment is monitored closely, so that melting points (where heat is absorbed) and glass transition temperatures can be observed. The glass transition temperature is the point at which the material becomes elastomeric (or rubbery); above this point, the elastic modulus and strength of the polymer can fall sharply (see ☑ **Viscoelasticity in thermoplastics** ☑). It is shown by a change in slope of the heating curve without any significant peak (as is found during melting or crystallization).

☑ Viscoelasticity in thermoplastics

The elastic modulus of thermoplastic polymers varies with both temperature and time, a property known as viscoelasticity. You may recall from Part 3 that viscoelasticity can be thought of as a combination of viscous and elastic behaviour. The viscous component is due to the polymer chains moving past one another in non-crystalline regions, and is time-dependent. The elastic component arises from the elastomeric behaviour of the amorphous chains plus, in partially crystalline polymers, the more nearly elastic response of the crystalline zones. These elastic contributions are reversible, so upon unloading they drive the viscous component in reverse, producing time-dependent recovery.

As a result, it is difficult to define a single value of elastic modulus for some polymers in the same way that such a value can be defined for a metal. Instead, what is specified is a ratio of stress to strain at a given time; this may be a creep modulus E_C or a stress relaxation modulus E_R, depending on the phenomenon that is being exhibited. For example, you might say that a particular grade of polystyrene has a ten-second relaxation modulus $E_R(10 \text{ s})$ of 1.0 GPa at 0.1% strain.

When E_R is plotted as a function of temperature for a typical thermoplastic (polystyrene), curves of the form shown in Figure 6.38 are obtained. Curves A and B represent differing molecular weights. They demonstrate four typical regions of behaviour: a glassy region (below about 100 °C), a transition region (centred at about 100 °C), an elastomeric or rubbery region (120–140 °C) and a viscous flow region (above about 160 °C, depending on molecular weight). Characteristic curves for the cross-linked and crystalline forms of polystyrene are also shown in the figure: you will notice that there is no viscous flow region for the cross-linked material, as cross-linking prevents this type of behaviour from occurring.

▷

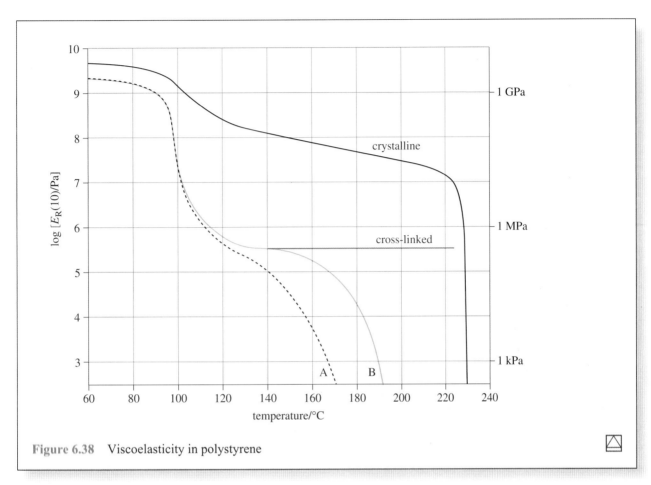

Figure 6.38   Viscoelasticity in polystyrene

This is perhaps best illustrated by looking at the results. Three samples of polypropylene were examined and produced the curves shown in Figure 6.39.

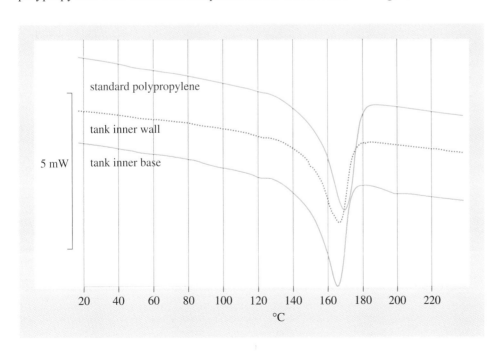

Figure 6.39
DSC curves from polypropylene samples, showing the melting points

One was a standard sample; the other two samples were taken from the tank inner wall and base liner respectively. They all show a very strong melting peak at 165–170 °C, indicating that they are reasonably similar in nature and composition. Three polyester samples from the type of GRP used in the tank outer shell were analysed in the same way, the results being shown in Figure 6.40. Again, one of these samples was a standard, whereas the other two were from the wall and base of the tank. These curves also show a good correlation with one another, exhibiting a glass transition temperature of 60–80 °C.

SAQ 6.12 (Learning outcomes 6.4 and 6.6)

Looking at Figures 6.39 and 6.40, compare the operating temperature of the tank with the ability of the liner and shell to resist it.

It is clear from the answer to SAQ 6.12 that whereas the liner could well resist the temperature of the contents, the polyester matrix of the shell would have been above its glass transition temperature – and so elastomeric – during most of the lifetime of the tank. The consequences of elastomeric behaviour would have been serious for the integrity of the shell, simply because the tensile stiffness of an elastomer is very much lower than that of the equivalent glassy solid. The tensile modulus of a typical rubber is about 3 MPa, well below that of the equivalent glassy solid, which is about 3 GPa – one thousand times higher. The shell could, therefore, be expected to deform and creep under the hoop stress of a tank kept highly filled. Although the GRP as a whole would have had a substantially stiffer modulus, of about 200 GPa, the elastomeric behaviour of the polyester matrix would have meant that the material responded to applied loads as though it were of very much lower stiffness.

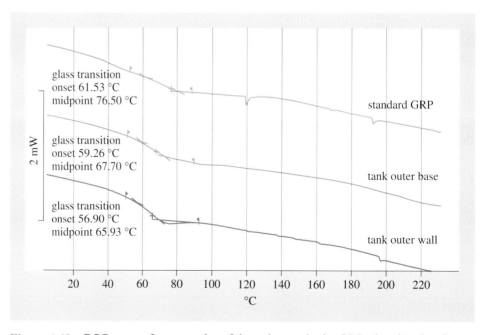

Figure 6.40   DSC curves from samples of the polyester in the GRP, showing the glass transition temperatures

As well as the high operating temperature of the tank, the heating and cooling of its contents should be considered. Over the lifetime of the tank, there were several occasions when the temperature of the contents changed quite rapidly (as shown in Figure 6.37). SAQ 6.13 considers the effect that this could have had on the tank wall.

SAQ 6.13 (Learning outcome 6.4 and Block 1 revision)

What effect would the change in the circumference of the tank, caused by the temperature of the contents rising from 20 to 90 °C, have on the stresses in the wall?

To answer this, you need to consider the fact that the wall is made from two materials that have different thermal properties: the coefficient of thermal expansion for polypropylene is 80×10^{-6} K^{-1}, but for the GRP used in the tank shell it is 20×10^{-6} K^{-1}.

Calculate the change in circumference for the two materials separately. The design diameter of the tank is 4.2 m (Figure 6.29), so the initial circumference at 20 °C is 4.2 m $\times \pi \approx 13.2$ m. Use this initial circumference for both materials as a first approximation.

Use your answer to suggest what effect the change in temperature is likely to have on the hoop stress near the base of the tank. What would happen if the contents were cooled back down from 90 to 20 °C?

(Remember from Block 1 that the change in length ΔL of a sample is given by $\Delta L = \alpha L \times \Delta T \times L_0$ where αL is the thermal expansion coefficient of the material, ΔT is the change in temperature and L_0 is the original length of the sample.)

The answer to SAQ 6.13 shows that the effect of temperature variations in the contents of the tank would have been to increase the hoop stress in the wall and contribute to delamination failure, and is an example of how a change in temperature can introduce stresses into a system without any alteration to the applied loads.

4.3.8 Conclusions

It is now clear why the lower wall of the tank deformed so badly over its lifetime: the hot contents softened the shell to such an extent that it could not resist the hoop stresses imposed by the pressure of the nearly full tank. Although the liner was resistant to the operating temperatures of the tank, it too would creep: polypropylene has a relatively low modulus of about 1.5 GPa, much lower than that of the shell material. It is also susceptible to creep at high imposed stresses, the creep rate increasing with increase of temperature. If the shell could no longer resist the hoop stress near the base of the tank, then the liner will have deformed along with the shell.

There were additional problems caused by the difference in thermal expansion between the liner and the outer shell, as shown by the delamination failure. This would have induced an additional tensile stress at the interface between the two layers. There was a cooling cycle just before the final failure, and it is likely that delamination occurred at the pipe junction, so putting the polypropylene liner under a high hoop stress. This caused the liner to fail along the vertical weld, the hoop stress being transferred to the GRP shell, which then failed rapidly owing to the stress-raising effects of the hole. The fluid contents then impacted the bund wall, which failed in turn, and the many brittle cracks throughout the structure grew to completion, wrecking the facility.

The design of the tank was clearly not sufficient to cope with its normal working conditions. Its walls were of insufficient thickness to resist normal working pressures from the contents, and the working temperature of 90 °C was above the heat distortion temperature of the GRP shell. Further enquiries failed to determine whether the tank had actually been water tested before installation, and whether or not this had been done without the bund wall in place, so that any distortion of the tank wall could be observed and reported. The bund wall, far from containing any leak, failed when impacted by the wave of fluid that was released suddenly from the main tank. It also prevented the bulging of the main wall from being seen and remedial action being taken. Figure 6.41 shows how such tanks should be built.

SAQ 6.14 (Learning outcomes 6.4 and 6.6)

Describe the failure of the 100-tonne tank on Teesside, including a discussion of its principal defects and how those defects led to its collapse.

What tests should have been conducted on the tank before installation?

This case study and the one before it carry an important message: materials' properties and their response to loads usually vary with temperature. Information on how a material will behave needs to be obtained for the correct combination of service temperature and environment if it is to be used sensibly for the development of a safe design.

Figure 6.41   Close-up of successful tanks at Immingham docks: the circumferential lines show the boundaries of extra GRP layers that provide reinforcement at the base of the wall. Note that the spillage on the ground has leaked from a pipe, not from the tank itself!

5 CODA

This brings us to the end of this course on structural integrity. The course has taken you from the basic concepts of stress and strain, and how external loads interact with the geometry of components to cause stresses; continued through the effects of cracks, and how we can design safely knowing that a component contains defects; looked at mechanisms that can lead to failure even when the applied loads do not exceed the design strength or toughness; and finished with a reminder that temperature is an important factor in determining a material's properties.

You should have learned from this course the importance of understanding the effects of stress on a material, and how factors such as how one component is joined to another can affect the stresses that are generated. Even components that experience relatively low loads can still deteriorate over time because of fatigue or environmental conditions.

I hope that you have found this course to be both enjoyable and rewarding.

EXERCISE 6.5

To gauge the progress you have made, cast your mind back to the list of failures that I asked you to compile in the Introduction to Block 1 (Exercise 2). If you still have the list, run a critical eye over your relatively uninformed failure assessments. How would they be different if you carried them out again now?

LEARNING OUTCOMES

After studying Block 2 Part 6 you should be able to do the following.

6.1 Analyse problems involving bending stresses, given appropriate information.

6.2 Determine the longitudinal stresses in curved beams, with various cross sections, that are subjected to bending moments.

6.3 Use stress analysis to help make design decisions concerning the geometry of a simple engineering component.

6.4 Use stress analysis concepts to analyse failures.

6.5 Use creep data in developing designs.

6.6 Assess a design against the appropriate standards.

ANSWERS TO EXERCISES

EXERCISE 6.1

First, the British Standard design has a much shorter neck region. Considering that the neck experiences relatively low stresses, approximately equal to the direct tensile stress, there is no need for it to be very long – the extended neck region in our design is simply a waste of material. Note that the tip of the hook is also thinner, and circular, in the British Standard design, since the stresses here are also small.

Second, in the British Standard design the inner radius is smaller, proportionally – it is much less than the width of the curved beam. In our design the inner radius is equal to the beam width. The latter has the effect of placing more material further away from the centre of curvature, thus increasing the bending moment and, hence, the bending stresses that arise.

EXERCISE 6.2

Recall that the absolute temperature in kelvin is related to the temperature in degrees Celsius by the equation $T/\text{K} = \theta/°\text{C} + 273$.

(a) $T_m = (1400 + 273)\,\text{K} = 1673\,\text{K}$, and the operating temperature T is $(650 + 273)\,\text{K}$ $= 923\,\text{K}$. So $T_H = 923\,\text{K}/1673\,\text{K} = 0.55$.

(b) $T_m = (190 + 273)\,\text{K} = 463\,\text{K}$, and T is $(25 + 273)\,\text{K} = 298\,\text{K}$. So $T_H = 298\,\text{K}/463\,\text{K} = 0.64$.

(c) $T_m = (540 + 273)\,\text{K} = 813\,\text{K}$, and T is $(25 + 273)\,\text{K} = 298\,\text{K}$. So $T_H = 298\,\text{K}/813\,\text{K} = 0.37$.

(d) $T_m = (130 + 273)\,\text{K} = 403\,\text{K}$, and T is $(25 + 273)\,\text{K} = 298\,\text{K}$. So $T_H = 298\,\text{K}/403\,\text{K} = 0.74$.

Of these four examples, only the aluminium alloy at room temperature is unlikely to undergo creep. The other three materials are operating at temperatures above $0.4T_m$, so the possibility of creep cannot be ignored.

EXERCISE 6.3

In practice, there will be a biaxial stress state in the pipe wall, so a uniaxial tensile test may produce different modes of failure; creep rates are highly dependent on the three-dimensional state of stress, for example. Also, if there are residual stresses in the pipe from the manufacturing process, then testing a real pipe is more likely to give an accurate result.

EXERCISE 6.4

Given that the inner liner shown in Figure 6.30 is 6 mm thick, the outer GRP shell must be just over 9 mm thick at the right, but only about 7.5 mm thick at the left (next to the corner). The former is equivalent to about six layers, the latter to five layers (7.5 mm/1.5 mm = 5).

EXERCISE 6.5

As before, this is a personal list and I am unable to comment on it specifically; but hopefully you will feel rather pleased with the knowledge you have acquired and with the improved rigour of your structural integrity assessment.

ANSWERS TO SELF-ASSESSMENT QUESTIONS

SAQ 6.1

(a) Rearranging Equation (6.1), we have:

$$\sigma = \frac{My}{I}$$

The bending moment M is equal to the force F multiplied by the distance from the centre of curvature to the centroid of the beam:

$$M = F\left(\frac{r_o + r_i}{2}\right) = 10 \times 10^3 \text{ N} \times 45 \times 10^{-3} \text{ m} = 450 \text{ N m}$$

The second moment of area is given by:

$$I = \frac{bh^3}{12} = \frac{12 \times 10^{-3} \text{ m} \times \left(30 \times 10^{-3} \text{ m}\right)^3}{12} = 2.70 \times 10^{-8} \text{ m}^4$$

For the straight-beam approximation, it is assumed that the neutral surface coincides with the centroid of the section. So, the maximum stress occurs at the inner radius where $y = 15 \times 10^{-3}$ m:

$$\sigma = \frac{My}{I} = \frac{450 \text{ N m} \times 15 \times 10^{-3} \text{ m}}{2.70 \times 10^{-8} \text{ m}^4} = 250 \text{ MPa}$$

Similarly the minimum stress is at the outer radius, i.e. $y = -15 \times 10^{-3}$ m, so:

$$\sigma = -250 \text{ MPa}$$

(b) The tensile stress due to the 10 kN force acting over the 30 mm by 12 mm rectangular cross section at AB is:

$$(10 \times 10^3 \text{ N})/(30 \times 10^{-3} \text{ m} \times 12 \times 10^{-3} \text{ m}) = 28 \text{ MPa}$$

Hence at the inner radius the total stress is:

$$250 + 28 = 278 \text{ MPa}$$

and at the outer radius the total stress is:

$$-250 + 28 = -222 \text{ MPa}$$

SAQ 6.2

The stress due to bending is given by:

$$\sigma = \frac{My}{Ae(r_n - y)}$$

where, referring to Figures 6.2 and 6.5:

$$A = 12 \times 10^{-3}\,\text{m} \times 30 \times 10^{-3}\,\text{m} = 3.6 \times 10^{-4}\,\text{m}^2$$

$$M = FR = 10 \times 10^3\,\text{N} \times 45 \times 10^{-3}\,\text{m} = 450\,\text{N m}$$

$$r_n = \frac{h}{\ln\left(\dfrac{r_o}{r_i}\right)} = \frac{30\,\text{mm}}{\ln\left(\dfrac{60}{30}\right)} = 43.28\,\text{mm}$$

$$e = R - r_n = 45\,\text{mm} - 43.28\,\text{mm} = 1.72\,\text{mm}$$

Hence at the inner radius, where $y = r_n - r_i = 13.28$ mm:

$$\sigma = \frac{450\,\text{N m} \times 13.28 \times 10^{-3}\,\text{m}}{3.6 \times 10^{-4}\,\text{m}^2 \times 1.72 \times 10^{-3}\,\text{m} \times (43.28 - 13.28) \times 10^{-3}\,\text{m}} = 322\,\text{MPa}$$

and at the outer radius, where $y = r_n - r_o = -16.72$ mm:

$$\sigma = \frac{450\,\text{N m} \times -16.72 \times 10^{-3}\,\text{m}}{3.6 \times 10^{-4}\,\text{m}^2 \times 1.72 \times 10^{-3}\,\text{m} \times (43.28 + 16.72) \times 10^{-3}\,\text{m}} = -203\,\text{MPa}$$

As before, there is an extra tensile stress of 28 MPa due to the applied load, so at the inner radius the total stress is:

$$322 + 28 = 350\,\text{MPa}$$

and at the outer radius the total stress is

$$-203 + 28 = -175\,\text{MPa}$$

SAQ 6.3

As it stands, the magnitude of the tensile stresses at the inner radius (350 MPa) is significantly higher than the magnitude of the compressive stresses at the outer radius (175 MPa). Both types of stress can cause yielding, but tensile stresses also promote crack growth, which makes them more dangerous. For this reason, it makes sense to put more material near where the large tensile stresses are expected and less in the compressive region. A tapered cross section, wider at the inner radius than at the outer radius, would be suitable.

SAQ 6.4

First compute the parameters for use in the bending equation for curved beams, using the information in Figures 6.5 and 6.7 (the cross-sectional area A has been designed to be the same as before, i.e. 3.6×10^{-4} m^2):

$$R = r_i + \frac{h\left(b_i + 2b_o\right)}{3\left(b_i + b_o\right)} = \left[30 + \frac{30}{3}\frac{\left(18 + 12\right)}{\left(18 + 6\right)}\right] \text{mm} = 42.5 \text{ mm}$$

$$M = FR = 10 \times 10^3 \text{ N} \times 42.5 \times 10^{-3} \text{ m} = 425 \text{ N m}$$

$$r_n = \frac{A}{b_o - b_i + \left[\frac{\left(b_i r_o - b_o r_i\right)}{h}\right]\ln\left(\frac{r_o}{r_i}\right)}$$

$$= \frac{3.6 \times 10^{-4} \text{ m}^2}{\left(6 - 18\right) \times 10^{-3} \text{ m} + \left[\frac{\left(18 \times 60 - 6 \times 30\right) \times 10^{-6} \text{ m}^2}{30 \times 10^{-3} \text{ m}}\right]\ln\left(\frac{60}{30}\right)}$$

$$= 40.94 \text{ mm}$$

$$e = R - r_n = 42.5 \text{ mm} - 40.94 \text{ mm} = 1.56 \text{ mm}$$

The maximum bending stress is at the inner radius, where $y = r_n - r_i = 10.94$ mm:

$$\sigma = \frac{My}{Ae\left(r_n - y\right)}$$

$$= \frac{425 \text{ N m} \times 10.94 \times 10^{-3} \text{ m}}{3.6 \times 10^{-4} \text{ m}^2 \times 1.56 \times 10^{-3} \text{ m} \times \left(40.94 - 10.94\right) \times 10^{-3} \text{ m}}$$

$$= 276 \text{ MPa}$$

Adding the extra stress due to tensile loading (28 MPa) gives 304 MPa total stress.

If you repeated the calculation at the outer radius you would find that the bending stress there is about −240 MPa, giving a total minimum stress of −212 MPa.

SAQ 6.5

Recall that, in general, the sign of the residual stress caused by non-uniform deformation will be opposite to the sign of the plastic strain that produced it. Hence, yielding and plastic flow in tension will give rise to a local compressive residual stress at the inner radius.

More specifically, when proof loading causes yield at the inner part of the beam the stress there will be limited to the yield stress of the steel, say around 400 MPa. On unloading, elastic recovery of the nearby material will push this part of the hook into compression. The magnitude of this compressive stress is typically equivalent to the maximum expected tensile stress during proof stressing (around 500 MPa for our hook design), diminished by the yield stress of 400 MPa – a net final residual stress of around 100 MPa in compression.

SAQ 6.6

Perpendicular to the largest principal stress (the hoop stress), i.e. along the axis of the pipe.

SAQ 6.7

(a) From Figure 6.13, the HDPE at 20 °C has a creep lifetime of:

   (i) $10^{6.2}$ hours or approximately 180 years at 5 MPa

   (ii) $10^{7.1}$ hours or approximately 1440 years at 3 MPa.

(b) To allow a 50-year life for the pipe operating at 20 °C, the stress should have an upper limit of 7 MPa.

SAQ 6.8

From Figure 6.25, the diameter of the tank is approximately 21 m, and it is 15 m high with a 17 mm thick wall. The pressure at the base of the tank is thus given by:

$$p = h\rho g = 15 \text{ m} \times 1500 \text{ kg m}^{-3} \times 9.81 \text{ m s}^{-2} = 221 \text{ kPa}$$

and the hoop stress is then given by:

$$\sigma_h = pr/t = (221 \text{ kPa} \times 11.5 \text{ m})/0.017 \text{ m} = 150 \text{ MPa}$$

This value is about seven times smaller than the strength of steel, which is 1100 MPa, so a stress raiser with a stress concentration factor K_t of about 7 would be needed to initiate fracture. You may recall from Block 2 Part 3 that a circular hole contributes a K_t value of approximately 3, so another stress raiser is needed to explain the failure.

The tank was manufactured from plates riveted together, and the additional stress concentration at the rivet holes may have been the critical factor. Joints at the edges of holes act as further stress raisers, the net effect being not the sum of the two separate stress concentration factors, but their product. Thus, a semicircular hole in the edge of a larger semicircular hole will have a K_t of $3 \times 3 = 9$, which would have been high enough to initiate fracture in this case.

SAQ 6.9

Since the hoop stress acts circumferentially, it is the vertical welds that are the most critical. The horizontal welds are acted on by the longitudinal stress, which is only half the magnitude of the hoop stress.

SAQ 6.10

Comparing the data from the specification with the information given in Table 6.2:

Contents	Could be acid or alkali from other parts of the chemical plant, so 'highly corrosive'	Category I
Compatibility of liner with contents	The polypropylene used is resistant to acid/alkali	Category III
Design temperature	Design temperature is 90 °C	Category I or II depending on HDT of resin
Design pressure	Static head	Category III
Size of tank	From Figure 6.29, size of tank > 50 m^3	Category I
Geometry	Flat bottom, full support	Category III
Other criteria	Tank is safety-critical, because if it fails then workers could be injured	Category I

So out of seven criteria, at least three demand that the design be a Category I tank, requiring independent approval and calculations covering hydrostatic loading, lifting arrangements, etc. Full records of manufacture should have been kept, and the final tank should have been tested and inspected by an independent qualified engineer.

The tank was assigned Category III in the specification, which is not justified by its function and design: fewer than half the assessment criteria placed the tank in Category III.

SAQ 6.11

Figure 6.29 gives all the dimensions needed to calculate the volume V:

$$V = \pi r^2 h = \pi \times (2.1 \text{ m})^2 \times 6.5 \text{ m} = 90.05 \text{ m}^3$$

So for a maximum weight of 104 tonnes, the maximum density of the contents is given by:

$$\rho = m/V = 1.04 \times 10^5 \text{ kg}/90.05 \text{ m}^{-3} = 1155 \text{ kg m}^{-3}$$

The hoop stress at the base of the tank is calculated from the maximum pressure at the base of the tank:

$$p = h\rho g = 6.5 \text{ m} \times 1155 \text{ kg m}^{-3} \times 9.81 \text{ m s}^{-2} = 73.65 \text{ kPa}$$

The hoop stress is then given by:

$$\sigma_h = pr/t = (73.65 \text{ kPa} \times 2.1 \text{ m})/0.009 \text{ m} = 17.2 \text{ MPa}$$

Given that the tensile strength of the CSM is between 55 and 117 MPa, the safety factor falls nominally in the range 3.2 to 6.8, depending on the quality of the laminate. This seems to be a reasonable safety factor. However, note that the strength of the material might be lower at 90 °C.

SAQ 6.12

The polypropylene samples all show a melting point well in excess of the maximum working temperature of the tank, so the liner is capable of retaining its integrity.

The polyester matrix contained in the shell GRP, however, would be in excess of its glass transition temperature above about 70 °C, which is below the tank's normal working temperature of 80–95 °C.

SAQ 6.13

The change in temperature ΔT is 90 °C – 20 °C = 70 °C, which is equivalent to a change of 70 K.

For the polypropylene:

$$\Delta L = 80 \times 10^{-6} \text{ K}^{-1} \times 70 \text{ K} \times 13.2 \text{ m} = 0.074 \text{ m or } 74 \text{ mm}$$

For the GRP:

$$\Delta L = 20 \times 10^{-6} \text{ K}^{-1} \times 70 \text{ K} \times 13.2 \text{ m} = 0.018 \text{ m or } 18 \text{ mm}$$

So clearly, the polypropylene used to make the liner of the tank undergoes a much greater expansion under heating than the GRP used to make the shell.

The liner must therefore have exerted substantial pressure on the shell when the contents of the tank were being heated, acting to increase the hoop stress in the wall.

At high temperature, the shell would relax some of this stress by creep, but then on cooling, the liner would shrink more quickly than the shell, putting the interface between the two components into tension and so leading to delamination between the two materials.

SAQ 6.14

A 100-tonne storage tank failed catastrophically less than two years after construction and installation at a chemical works on Teesside. It was part of a catalyst-polishing unit, and was used to store and mix acid and alkali washes. It was designed for a full-capacity load of 104 tonnes at a temperature of 90 °C. It was a Category I tank under BS 4994:1987, but had been wrongly assigned Category III status.

The tank structure comprised a polypropylene liner supported by a GRP shell. Although the liner was 6 mm thick throughout the tank, the shell was thinner at the crucial sides than, for example, in the centre of the base. A large outlet pipe near the base intersected with a vertical weld in the liner.

The tank failed by delamination at the outlet pipe caused by creep of the walls nearby under the hydrostatic load of the very hot contents. The inner and outer walls had quite different physical properties: the liner was a thermoplastic with a high melting point of about 170 °C, but the shell consisted of a CSM glass–polyester composite with a glass transition temperature of about 70 °C. This meant that the shell was elastomeric when it passed 70 °C, and crept rapidly as a direct result. During a heating cycle, the liner would expand against the shell, putting it under a greater hoop stress than hydrostatic pressure alone. In the cooling part of a cycle, the liner would shrink back from the shell, so creating a tensile stress at right angles to the wall thickness. Adhesion between the two materials was poor, so delamination occurred.

Numerous tests should have been conducted on the tank prior to installation, including tensile testing of all materials under the projected conditions of usage and, most critically, hydrostatic testing of the complete tank before the bund was fitted. Water at 90 °C should have been used in the test, and the wall condition monitored for at least 24 hours.

ACKNOWLEDGEMENTS

Grateful acknowledgement is made to the following sources:

FIGURES

Figure 6.8: Permission to reproduce extract from the BS 2903:1980 is granted by BSI. British Standards can be obtained from BSI Customer Services, 389 Chiswick High Road, London W4 4AL. Tel: +44 (0) 20 8996 9001.

Figure 6.11: Greig, J.M. (1976) 'A Typical Ductile Creep Rupture in MDPE Pipe', *The Use of Large Diameter PE Pipelines*, Lattice Intellectual Property Limited.

Figure 6.12: Courtesy of Hostalen Polyethylene UK Ltd.

Figure 6.14: Courtesy of GKN Westland Helicopters Ltd.

Figure 6.15: Courtesy of Alcoa Technical Center.

Figure 6.19: Taken from http://homepage.eircom.net/~steven/rn.htm.

Figure 6.20: Hull, D.J. (1981) *An Introduction to Composite Materials*, Cambridge University Press.

Figures 6.21–6.23: Lewis, P.R. and Weidmann, G.W. (1999) 'Catastrophic failure of a polypropylene tank part 1: primary investigation', *Engineering Failure Analysis*, vol. 6, pp. 197–214, © Elsevier.

Figure 6.25: Puleo, A. (2004) 'Location of the Tank and the Resulting Damage', *Dark Tide: the Great Boston Molasses Flood of 1919*, Beacon Press.

Figure 6.26: From Hull, D. (1999) *Fractography*, Figure 10.46, © Cambridge University Press.

Figures 6.27–6.37 and 6.39–6.41: © Peter Lewis.

Figure 6.38: Tobolsky, A.V. (1962) 'Variation of Stress Relaxation Modulus of Polystyrene with Temperature', *Properties and Structures of Polymers*, John Wiley & Sons Limited.

COURSE TEAM ACKNOWLEDGEMENTS

This part was prepared for the course team by Salih Gungor, Martin Rist, Peter Lewis and Michael Fitzpatrick.

T357 COURSE TEAM

Dr Michael Fitzpatrick (course team chair)

Andy Harding (course manager)

Jackie Burnicle (course manager)

ACADEMIC STAFF

Dr Alun Armstrong

Professor Adrian Demaid

Professor Chris Earl

Professor Lyndon Edwards

Dr Salih Gungor

Michael Hush

Dr Peter Lewis

Dr Jim Moffatt

Dr Ed Murphy

Dr Martin Rist

EXTERNAL ASSESSOR

Professor Lindsay Greer, University of Cambridge

CONSULTANTS

Professor Phil Irving, Cranfield University

SUPPORT STAFF

Debbie Derbyshire (course team secretary)

Colin Gagg

Stan Hiller

Gordon Imlach

Pete Ledgard

Sheila Taylor

PRODUCTION TEAM

Kirsten Barnett

Annette Booz

Philippa Broadbent

Lisa Carrick

Teresa Cox

Sarah Crompton

Daphne Cross

Anna Edgley-Smith

Vicky Eves

Chris French

Carol Houghton

Jonathan Martyn

Margaret McManus

Katie Meade

Lara Mynors

Deana Plummer

Lynn Short

Susanne Umerski